THE HUMAN BRAIN
a photographic guide

NEDZAD GLUHBEGOVIC, M.D., Ph.D.

Department of Anatomy and Embryology,
University of Utrecht, Utrecht, Holland

TERENCE H. WILLIAMS, M.D., Ph.D., D.Sc.

Professor and Head, Department of Anatomy,
College of Medicine,
The University of Iowa, Iowa City, Iowa

THE HUMAN BRAIN

a photographic guide

HARPER & ROW, PUBLISHERS
HAGERSTOWN

Cambridge
New York
Philadelphia
San Francisco

London
Mexico City
Sao Paulo
Sydney

1817

The authors and publisher have exerted every effort to ensure that drug selection and dosage set forth in this text are in accord with current recommendations and practice at the time of publication. However, in view of ongoing research, changes in government regulations, and the constant flow of information relating to drug therapy and drug reactions, the reader is urged to check the package insert for each drug for any change in indications and dosage and for added warnings and precautions. This is particularly important when the recommended agent is a new and/or infrequently employed drug.

80 81 82 83 84 85 10 9 8 7 6 5 4 3 2 1

THE HUMAN BRAIN: A Photographic Guide. Copyright © 1980 by Harper & Row, Publishers, Inc. All rights reserved. No part of this book may be used or reproduced in any manner whatsoever without written permission except in the case of brief quotations embodied in critical articles and reviews. Printed in the United States of America. For information address Medical Department, Harper & Row, Publishers, Inc., 2350 Virginia Avenue, Hagerstown, Maryland 21740.

Library of Congress Cataloging in Publication Data
Gluhbegovic, Nedzad.
  The human brain.
  Includes index.
  1. Brain—Atlases. 2. Spinal cord—Atlases. I. Williams, Terence H., joint author. II. Title.
QM455.G59 1980   612'.82'0222   79-19387
ISBN 0-06-140945-6

Contents

TO JOSEF KLINGLER AND
GEORGE ARCHIBALD GRANT MITCHELL

*The preparation method of Professor Klingler greatly influenced
the production of dissections showing inner structures of the
brain, and contributed most significantly to the success of the
examples illustrated in this volume.*

*Over many years, Professor Mitchell has been an esteemed
colleague in science, who led one of the authors (T.H.W.) into
research in the nervous system.*

Preface

THE HUMAN BRAIN: A PHOTOGRAPHIC GUIDE deals with the actual structure of the brain and spinal cord and their immediate coverings. Most of the preparations appear unstained as the anatomist displays them in a series of dissections. Each photograph is accompanied by a labeled drawing and descriptive text to help the reader in interpreting the salient points.

Even in a major course with practical classes, it is not realistic to expect the students to carry out the more complex brain dissections, though we hope to stimulate some to make the effort. The dissections, all newly prepared for this volume, can assist those students entering the field of human neuroanatomy for the first time to find out a great deal about the appearance and organization of the brain. The guide will also serve more advanced students, and teachers who may lack sufficient time or opportunity for carrying out the more complex and difficult dissections. It is our hope that this book will also help many clinicians to refresh and improve their knowledge of neuroanatomy, especially in regard to the arrangement of internal brain parts. It is also hoped, our preparations will reveal, to a certain degree at least, the exceptional beauty of the human brain.

This atlas displays the essential anatomy of the human central nervous system in five sections: Chapter 1 deals with the coverings, blood vessels, and the external and internal structure of the spinal cord; Chapter 2 relates to the coverings of the brain and the blood vessels that nourish it; Chapters 3 through 5 classify the brain dissections into three major collections, illustrating the cerebellum, brainstem, and cerebral hemispheres respectively. In our opinion, these dissections—some of which involve novel approaches—offer the student realistic perspectives about brain structure, which is not always the case with the artists' interpretations found in the majority of textbooks. We also believe that, when students are asked (after observing numerous brain sections) to reconstruct the organization mentally, some of them find this task difficult if not impossible. For this reason we have emphasized dissections of complex inner brain structures and their relationships, supplementing with sections that seem especially worthwhile and appropriate.

It will be seen that the same structure appears in several sections, so that by looking through a number of photographs the reader can gain a better idea of its appearance and relationships; this applies also to structures seen in sections of the spinal cord, brainstem, and cerebral hemispheres.

In general, the nomenclature used is based on the 4th Edition of the Nomina Anatomica: frontal, temporal, and occipital are used for the anterior, inferior, and posterior horns of the lateral ventricles; occipital forceps and frontal forceps have replaced forceps major and minor, respectively. Anterior and posterior have been largely changed to ventral and dorsal, and superior and inferior to cranial (or rostral) and caudal. We have considered revising the terminology for the branches of the cerebral vessels, cerebellar structures, and thalamic nuclei to conform to the latest Nomina Anatomica, but decided that at this time such a change could result in more difficulty than help, because many current texts, neurosurgeons, and neuroradiologists do not use all aspect of the new terminology. We hope that readers will not hesitate to inform us of their preferences in this or any other matter.

The larger portion of this collection of dissections is on display in the Anatomical Museum in Utrecht, Holland, and the remainder in the W. R. Ingram Memorial Learning Center, the Anatomy Department at the University of Iowa in Iowa City, Iowa, United States.

Many thoughtful colleagues have provided encouragement, advice, and constructive criticism in the course of this work. In particular, we wish to record our debt to Professor G. A. G. Mitchell (University of Manchester, U.K.) and the late Dr. W. R. Ingram (University of Iowa) who patiently checked drafts of the descriptions and made many important suggestions. For his valuable participation and enthusiasm we wish to thank Toine Voets, a senior medical student and student assistant in the Department of Anatomy at Utrecht, who prepared the spinal cord of a newborn infant, two additional gross specimens of the spinal cord, and assisted in the dissections illustrated in Figures 3-6 and 3-7.

It is evident that the authors have benefitted from the high degree of photographic skill available to them. Hans Kempkes of the Teaching Media Institute at the University of Utrecht, and his colleague Henk Zuidervaart, have shown great competence in their reproductions of the dissections in Holland; Paul Reimann has shown the same professionalism in his photographic work in Iowa City. It is important to acknowledge the adept assistance rendered by A. M. Van Egeraat, Senior Medical Illustrator in the Anatomy Department in Utrecht, for his line drawings carried with perceptiveness and unfailing enthusiasm, and to Evelyn Jew, Research Assistant in the Anatomy Department at the University of Iowa, for her assistance in the illustrations. Hans Kemperman, Chief Technician in the Anatomy Department in Utrecht, and Loren Spence, Coordinator of the Anatomical Gift Program at the University of Iowa, receive our thanks for carefully preserving this valuable material for dissection; and Ditrich Guse, Chief Technician in the Anatomy Department at Bochum, West Germany, receives our thanks for advice concerning tissue preservation.

It is a pleasure to extend our grateful thanks to Mrs. Dorothea Achterberg and Miss Mary Jo Thomann for their patient preparation of innumerable manuscripts. Finally, the staff of Harper and Row supplied inestimable general encouragement and abundant help.

T.W.

Methods Used in
Preparing the Specimens

For the preparations used to display the spinal cord, its covering membranes, the spinal nerve roots and ganglia, we had access to the body of a newborn male infant preserved in formaldehyde solution, together with adult material that had received prolonged treatment in the same preservative solution.

The human brains received careful postmortem attention, and those with gross defects were rejected from this study. We used the preservation method of Klingler, with minor adaptations. In removing the brain from the skull, every effort was made to minimize damage to the delicate surface. The organ was then suspended, by means of a ligature placed around the basilar artery, in a vessel containing 10% formaldehyde solution. This fluid was replaced after 24 hours and again after an interval of two weeks. After a total period of 4 weeks or longer in the formaldehyde solution, the brain was washed for several hours in cold running water.

Next it was placed in a plastic vessel containing 10% formaldehyde solution and stored for 8 days in a deep freeze at 25–30°C. At this point the brain was thawed under running cold water for 24 hours. Repeating the deep freezing procedure (in 10% formaldehyde solution) two or three times has been found to facilitate the subsequent dissection. After the last freezing, the brain can be kept in 5% formaldehyde solution indefinitely.

While the freezing method is an aid to dissection and generally increases the distinction between the grey and white matter of the brain, it does not produce absolutely consistent results, as Klingler himself acknowledged. As a rule, however, the technique described above makes it easier to prepare dissections of both fiber tracts and nuclei. We have observed that, in horizontal and coronal sections of the brain, satisfactory contrast between white and grey matter is achieved without using any stain.

For making the dissections, simple anatomic instruments were found to be quite satisfactory, fine forceps—straight or curved—being used to execute the delicate nerve bundle preparations. It was also necessary on most occasions to use the binocular loop or a dissecting stereomicroscope, together with lamps suitably placed to direct the light.

For the ten slides prepared by the Turtox Company, the preparation method is summarized as follows:

First, the brain is removed from the calvarium and put in 10% neutral formalin. The brainstem is then cut into blocks and each block stained by the Weigert method, following which it is embedded in celloidin. After the celloidin has thoroughly infiltrated the blocks and hardened, the blocks are ready for sectioning. (Sectioning is difficult and requires experience, because of the large size of the blocks.) As the sections are cut, they are floated onto alcohol, kept in proper order, and mounted on large glass slides. The sections are then allowed to dry slowly in a low-temperature oven for several weeks.

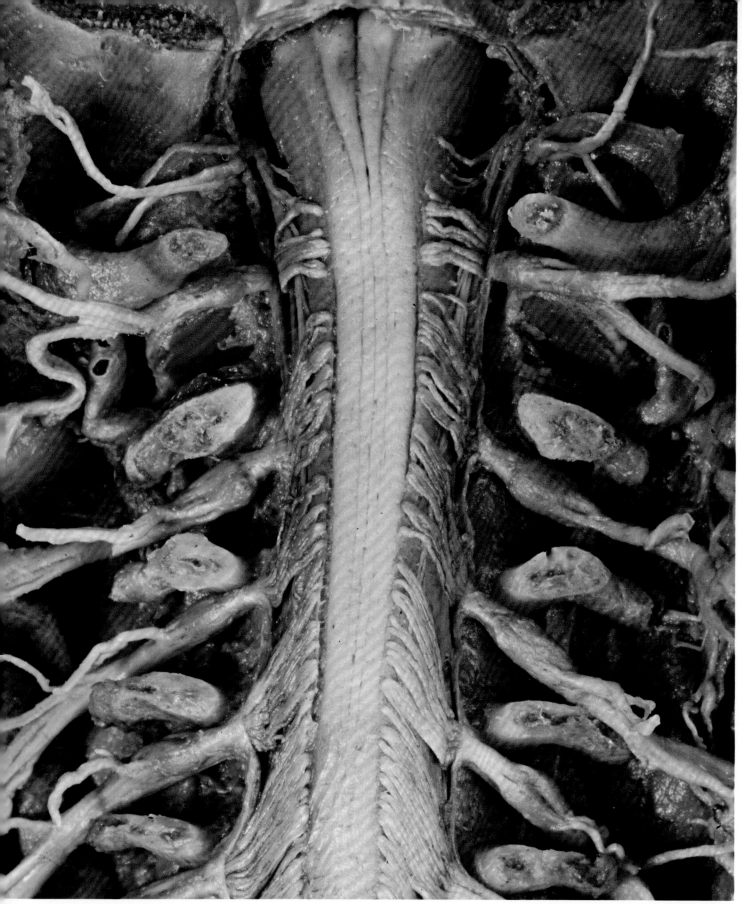

Fig. 1-3. Dorsal view of the lower part of the medulla oblongata and the upper six segments of the cervical spinal cord of a newborn infant (See legend for Fig. 1-3 on p. 7)

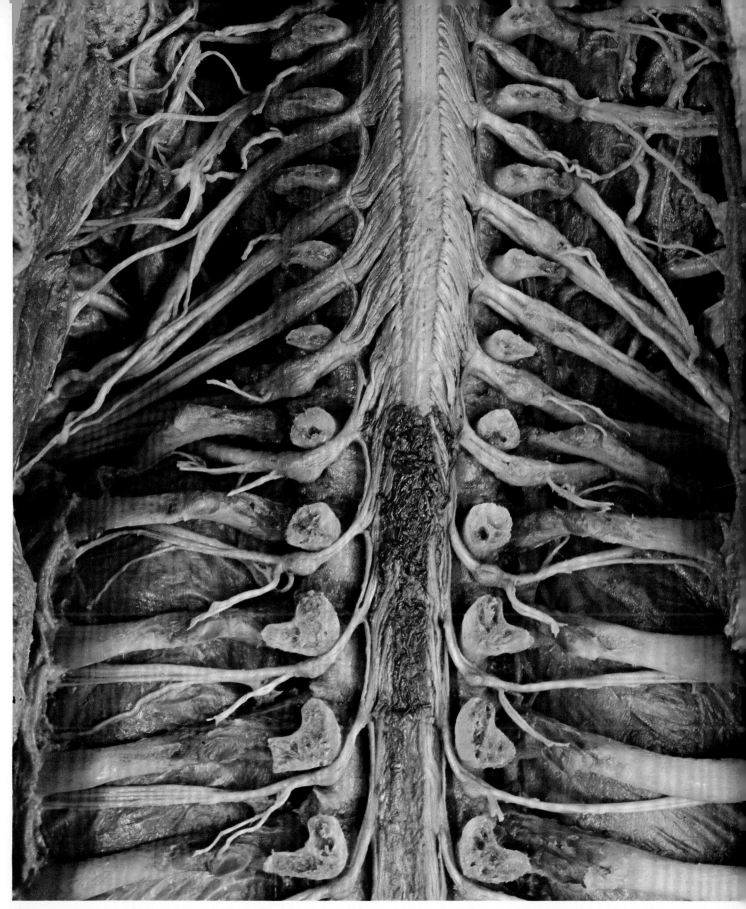

Fig. 1-4. Lower cervical and upper thoracic segments of the spinal cord of the newborn (See legend for Fig. 1-4 on p. 9)

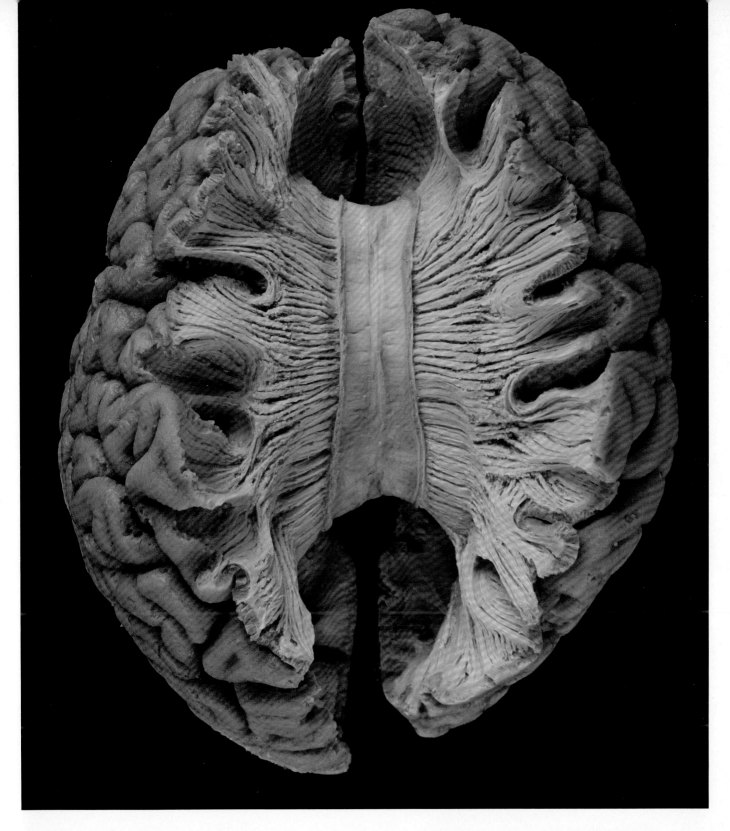

Fig. 5-21. Corpus callosum, its radiation, and indusium griseum displayed from above (See legend for Fig. 5-21 on p. 141)

◄ Fig. 5-10. Cortical projection systems of left cerebral hemisphere: medial aspect (See legend for Fig. 5-10 on p. 119)

◄ Fig. 5-11. Caudate nucleus, amygdaloid body, stria terminalis, corona radiata, and internal capsule: right cerebral hemisphere from the medial side (See legend for Fig. 5-11 on p. 121)

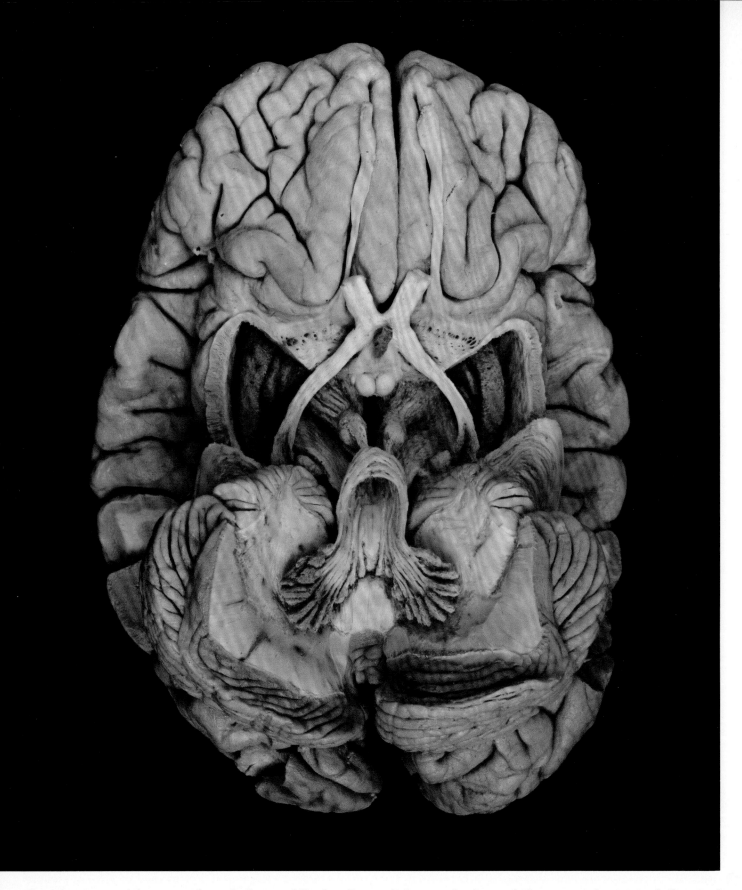

Fig. 5-23. Internal features of cerebellum, midbrain, diencephalon, and telencephalon: ventral aspect of dissected brain (See legend for Fig. 5-23 on p. 145)

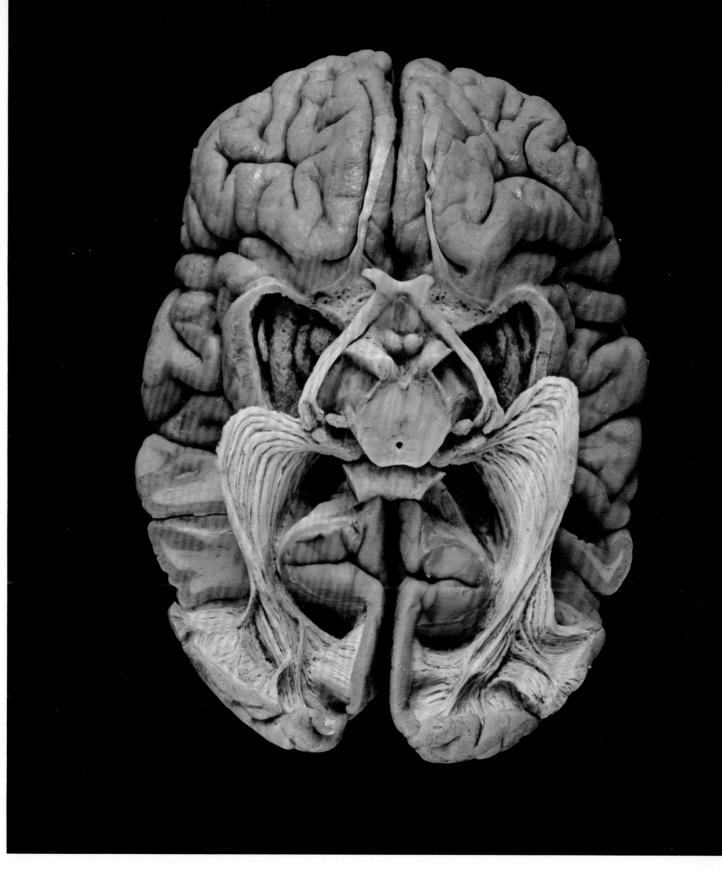

Fig. 5-24. Visual pathway from optic chiasma to occipital lobes, viewed from the basal aspect (See legend for Fig. 5-24 on p. 147)

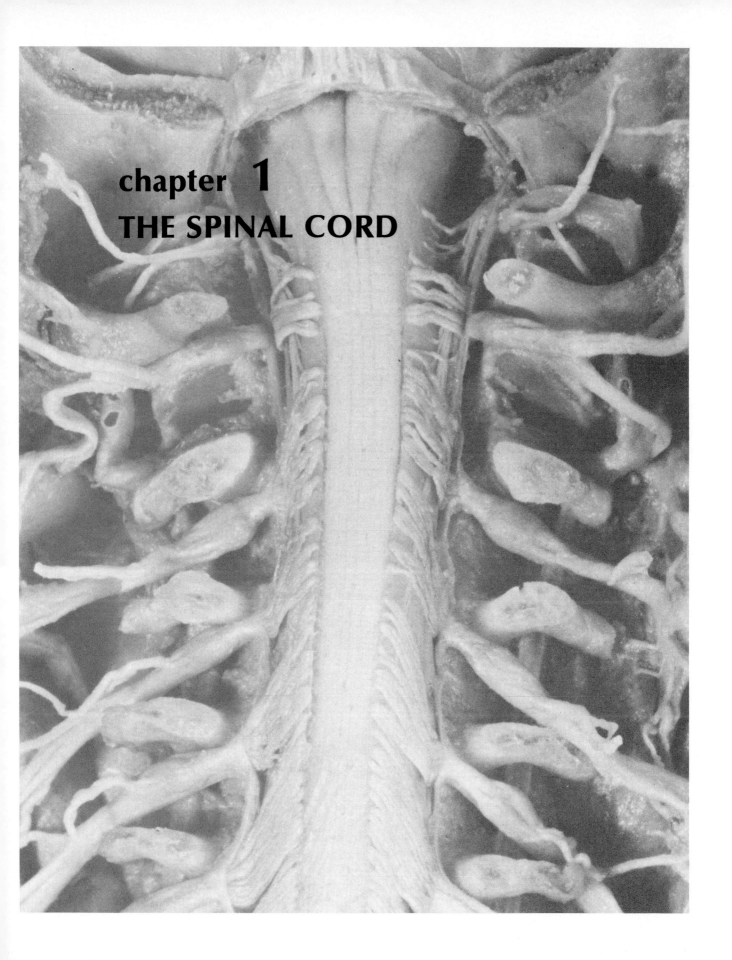

chapter **1**
THE SPINAL CORD

1-1 Cerebral and spinal dura mater of a newborn infant, dorsal view through the opened vertebral canal

The cerebral and spinal dura mater are continuous with one another at the foramen magnum of the occipital bone. At this level the outer layer of the dura is attached firmly to the margins of the foramen magnum. The pigmented areas of the outer surface of the cerebral dura mark the positions of the superior sagittal and transverse venous sinuses.

The spinal dura has a shiny appearance because we see only the inner, meningeal layer of the dura, there being no endosteal layer lining the vertebral canal. The roots of 31 pairs of spinal nerves emerge from the spinal cord. Attached to the dorsal, sensory roots of the spinal nerves are the spinal ganglia. Fusion of dorsal and ventral roots to form the spinal nerves occurs at the level of the intervertebral foramina, where they exist. The dura mater of the cord has tubular, sleevelike prolongations which ensheathe the roots of the spinal nerves together with the spinal nerves themselves, within the intervertebral foramina. These dural extensions are continuous distally with the epineurium of the spinal nerves. Note that the lower four cervical and the 1st thoracic, as well as the lower lumbar and upper sacral nerve roots and ganglia, are much larger than the rest. The larger spinal nerve roots and ganglia are associated with the cervical and lumbar enlargements of the spinal cord which provide limb innervation.

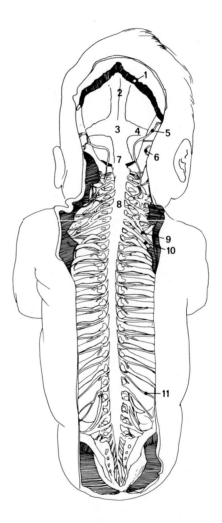

1. Posterior margin of parietal bone.
2. Superior sagittal sinus.
3. Confluens of sinuses.
4. Transverse sinus.
5. Greater occipital nerve.
6. Lesser occipital nerve.
7. Occipital sinus.
8. Spinal dura mater.
9. Superior trunk of brachial plexus.
10. Middle trunk of brachial plexus.
11. Subcostal nerve.

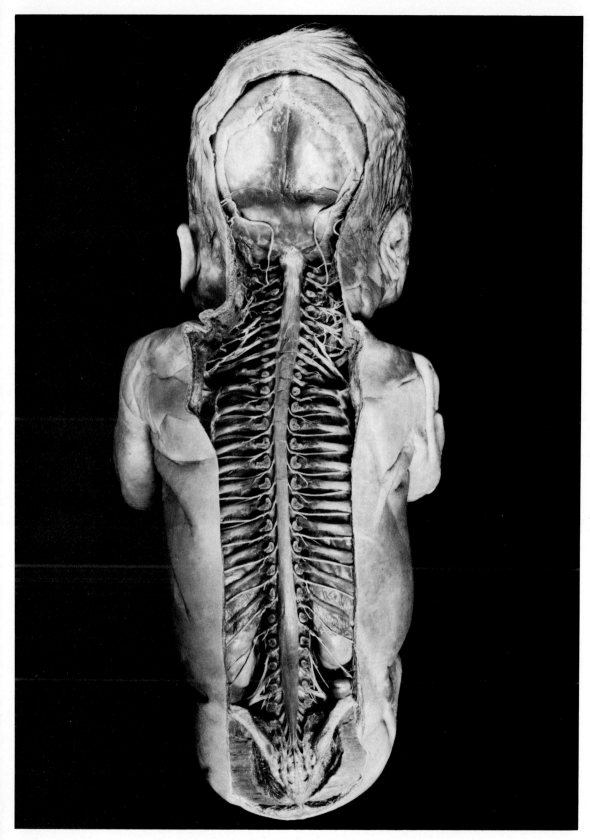

Figure 1-1.

1-2 Dural venous sinuses of a newborn infant exposed from the dorsal aspect

The dural sinuses of the newborn infant are very large in relation to the sizes of the skull and brain. In this preparation a dural septum, located slightly to the left of the midline, splits the terminal segment of the superior sagittal sinus into two parts, resulting in two parallel channels which are continuous with the paired transverse sinuses. The latter are the largest of the venous sinuses and are very important. The opening of the straight sinus, which travels in the line of union between the falx cerebri and the tentorium cerebelli, is seen to the right of the midline in this specimen.

The dilated meeting place of the superior sagittal, straight and paired transverse sinuses, known as the confluence of the sinuses, contains an arrangement of dural septa that fails to divide it completely. The occipital sinus, which is also subdivided by dural septa, commences at the confluence or its junction with the transverse sinus to enter and descend in the falx cerebelli. The occipital sinus communicates with parts of the basilar sinus, which show at the rim of the foramen magnum. The occipital lobes of the brain are exposed except for their covering of arachnoid mater and underlying pia, and they normally rest upon the tentorium cerebelli. Note the conspicuous greater occipital nerve—one of the thickest cutaneous nerves in the body*—arising from the posterior primary ramus of the 2nd cervical spinal nerve.

*In some bodies the saphenous nerve is larger!

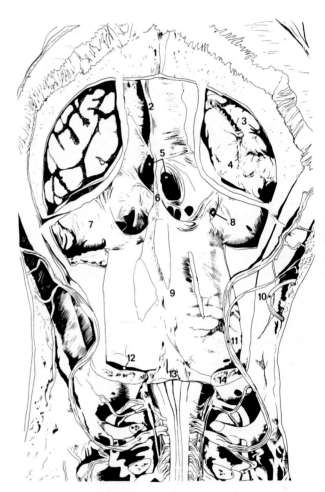

1. Cerebral dura mater.
2. Superior sagittal sinus.
3. Subdural space.
4. Occipital lobe of right cerebral hemisphere.
5. Straight sinus of tentorium.
6. Confluens of sinuses.
7. Transverse sinus.
8. Opening of superior cerebral vein into transverse sinus.
9. Occipital sinus.
10. Lesser occipital nerve.
11. Greater occipital nerve.
12. Part of basilar sinus.
13. Foramen magnum level.
14. Cut surface of occipital bone.

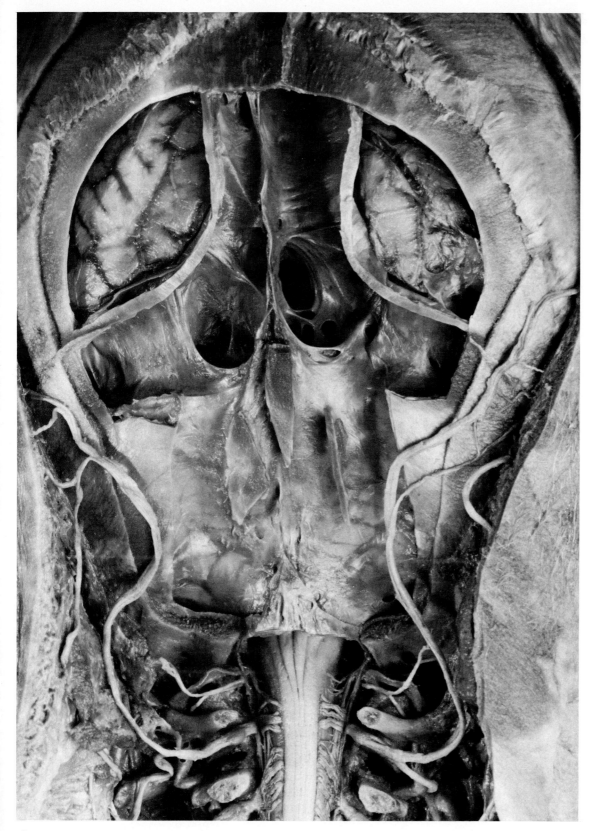

Figure 1-2.

Dorsal view of the lower part of the medulla oblongata and the upper six segments of the cervical spinal cord of a newborn infant

The posterior white columns (funiculi) lie alongside the posterior median sulcus. Their constituent bundles in the spinal cord can be followed upward without interruption into the lower closed part of the medulla oblongata. The 6th segment of the cervical cord has not been stripped of its pia mater. On each side of the posterior median sulcus are two longitudinally running fasciculi, the gracile and cuneate, separated by the shallow posterior intermediate sulcus. These fasciculi are composed of sensory axons that arise from cell bodies in the dorsal root ganglia of the spinal nerves and enter the spinal cord via the dorsal nerve roots. At the medullary level both fasciculi spread out and diverge from the median plane. Each terminates in an elongated and rather poorly defined swelling produced by the gracile or cuneate nucleus, in which the primary proprioceptive and exteroceptive fibers end and secondary axons—most of them carrying sensory signals onward to the thalamus—arise. Lateral to each fasciculus cuneatus an extensive series of dorsal nerve rootlets can be seen alongside the posterior lateral sulcus of the spinal cord. Each group of dorsal nerve rootlets is associated with the corresponding segmental nerve. Note that the upper rootlets run almost transversely, but that the lower ones become progressively longer and more oblique. From its beginning at the 5th cervical segment, the spinal root of the accessory nerve gains in thickness as fibers join it from higher segments. The root lies dorsal to the rootlets of the 1st cervical nerve and the vertebral artery and can be followed through the foramen magnum into the cranial cavity.

On each side a series of spinal ganglia can be observed within the intervertebral foramina. The ganglion associated with the 1st cervical nerve is small and fusiform, and immediately below it is the ventral motor root of the 1st cervical nerve. The other cervical ganglia are larger. The nerve roots and ganglia are surrounded by tubular extensions of dura, which merges with the epineurium that envelops the spinal nerves. The 1st cervical nerves are related closely to the vertebral arteries. The latter ascends through the transverse foramina of the cervical vertebrae, as shown on the left side of the preparation.

1. Gracile tubercle.
2. Cuneate tubercle.
3. Posterior median sulcus.
4. Posterior intermediate sulcus.
5. Vertebral artery.
6. 1st cervical spinal ganglion.
7. Motor root of first cervical nerve.
8. Cut surface of posterior arch of atlas.
9. Accessory nerve.
10. Cuneate fascicle.
11. Gracile fascicle.
12. Posterior lateral sulcus.
13. Denticulate ligament.
14. Cut edge of dura.
15. Dorsal rootlets of 5th cervical nerve.
16. Pia mater.

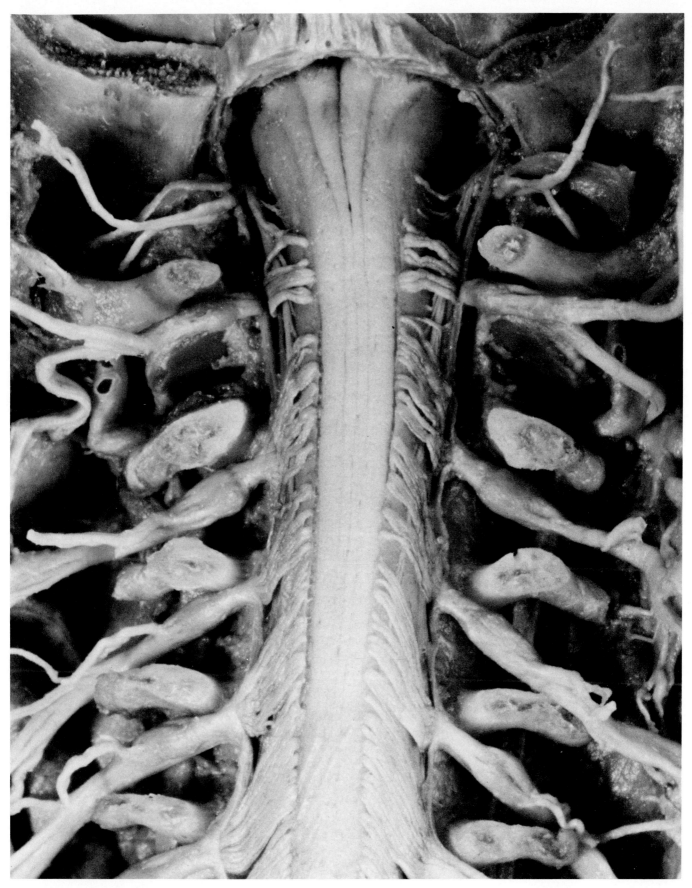

Figure 1-3. (Refer to color section, Fig. 1-3)

1-4 Lower cervical and upper thoracic segments of the spinal cord of the newborn

In the uppermost portion of this photograph, the pia mater has been removed to display the tracts of the posterior funiculi (gracilis and cuneatus). Below this, the spinal cord retains its thin, transparent, pial covering. In the next part, the abundant spinal veins in the subarachnoidal space are also retained. These veins are tortuous and bulky, making it virtually impossible to identify the spinal arteries. In the most caudal part of the spinal cord illustrated, the arachnoid mater has been left intact. It is a thin and transparent membrane through which the spinal vessels can be seen.

The cervical enlargement of the spinal cord extends from the 4th cervical to the 2nd thoracic segments. Closely packed dorsal rootlets issue from the cervical enlargement in orderly array, coalescing to form large dorsal roots which enter the spinal ganglia, which are also large. If the illustration were to extend a little more laterally, it would be even more obvious that the large anterior rami of the last four cervical and the 1st thoracic spinal nerves participate in the formation of the main trunks of the brachial plexus. Below the cervical enlargement, the dorsal rootlets, roots and ganglia diminish rapidly in size.

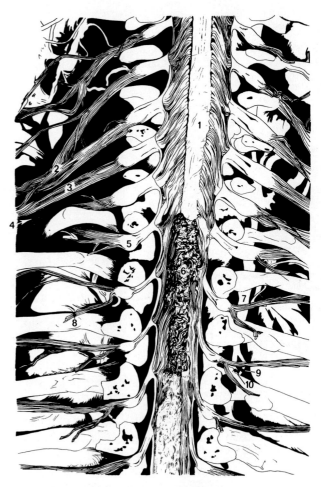

1. Cervical enlargement of spinal cord.
2. Superior trunk of brachial plexus.
3. Middle trunk of brachial plexus.
4. Inferior trunk of brachial plexus.
5. 1st thoracic spinal ganglion.
6. Blood vessels in subarachnoidal space.
7. Sympathetic trunk.
8. Dorsal ramus of second thoracic nerve.
9. Gray communicant ramus.
10. White communicant ramus.

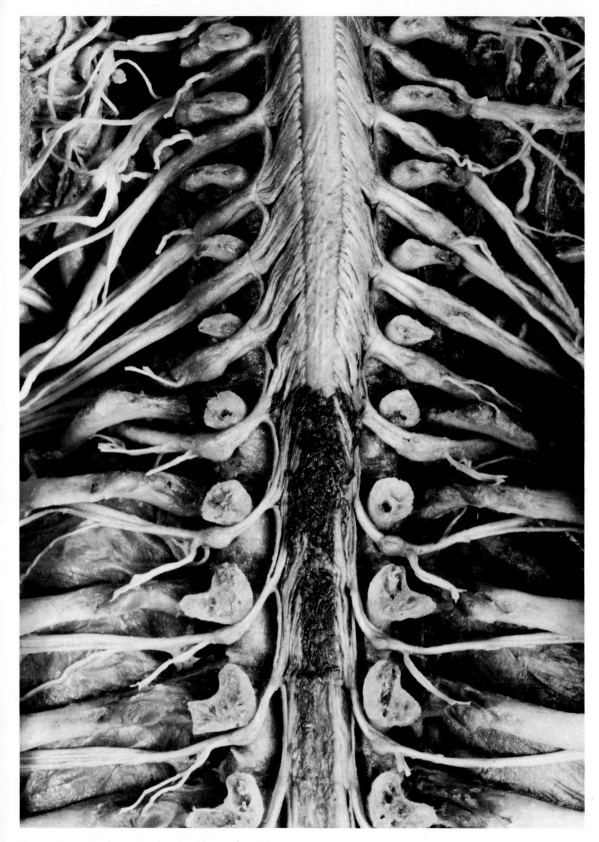

Figure 1-4. (Refer to color section, Fig. 1-4)

1-5 Lower thoracic and lumbar segments of the spinal cord of a newborn child

In the upper part of the photograph, numerous spinal vessels can be seen through the arachnoid mater. All the meninges (including the dura mater) have been preserved in the middle portion, while in the lower part all meninges have been removed (except pia mater) to show the lumbar enlargement of the spinal cord. Note the high obliquity of the dorsal rootlets as well as the increased size of the spinal nerve roots and ganglia at the level of the lumbar enlargement. In most cases, both dorsal (sensory) and ventral (motor) roots can be seen, the dorsal or sensory root being consistently larger. The intercostal muscles and vessels have been removed to display the intercostal nerves. Anterior to the ribs is the thin, shiny parietal pleura of the lung.

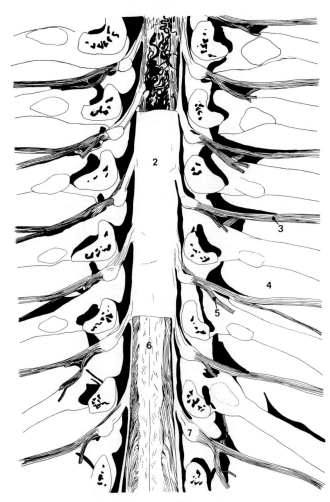

1. Arachnoid mater.
2. Dura mater.
3. 8th intercostal nerve.
4. Parietal pleura.
5. Dorsal ramus of 9th thoracic nerve.
6. Pia mater.
7. 11th thoracic spinal ganglion.

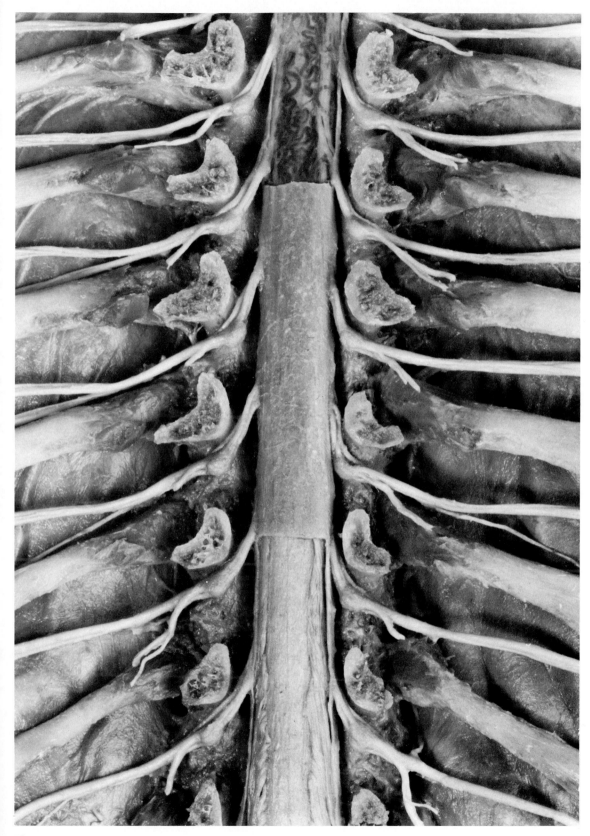

Figure 1-5.

1-6 Conus medullaris and cauda equina of a newborn infant: dorsal view

The lower end of the spinal cord narrows to form the conus medullaris, seen as the pale, pointed structure in the uppermost part of the photograph. In the newborn, the conus is located at the level of the upper margin of the 3rd lumbar vertebra, whereas as in the adult it is usually found at a level between the 1st and 2nd lumbar vertebrae. The filum terminale, a thin connective tissue filament which originates from the pial investment of the conus medullaris, is obscured by the cascade of descending lumbar, sacral, and coccygeal spinal nerve roots known as the cauda equina. In the lower part of the picture note the external part of the filum terminale covered by the dura. The filum descends in company with two coccygeal nerves and is connected to the 3rd, 4th, and 5th sacral vertebrae, and its terminal part is fused to the periosteum at the base of the coccygeal bone.

Note the thin, cut edges of the dural sheath outside the cauda equina, and the tubular dural sleeves around individual spinal nerves and ganglia. The lumbar and upper sacral ganglia are large and in some instances are bilobular or multilobular. Features of the lumbar plexus, including the formation of its main branches, can be observed.

1. Conus medullaris.
2. Iliohypogastric nerve.
3. Pelviureteric junction.
4. Ilioinguinal nerve.
5. Posterior surface of right kidney.
6. Lateral cutaneous nerve of thigh.
7. Cauda equina.
8. Descending colon.
9. Femoral nerve.
10. 5th lumbar spinal nerve ganglion.
11. Obturator nerve.
12. 1st sacral dorsal foramen.
13. Coccygeal nerve.
14. Gluteus maximus muscle.
15. Termination of filum terminale.

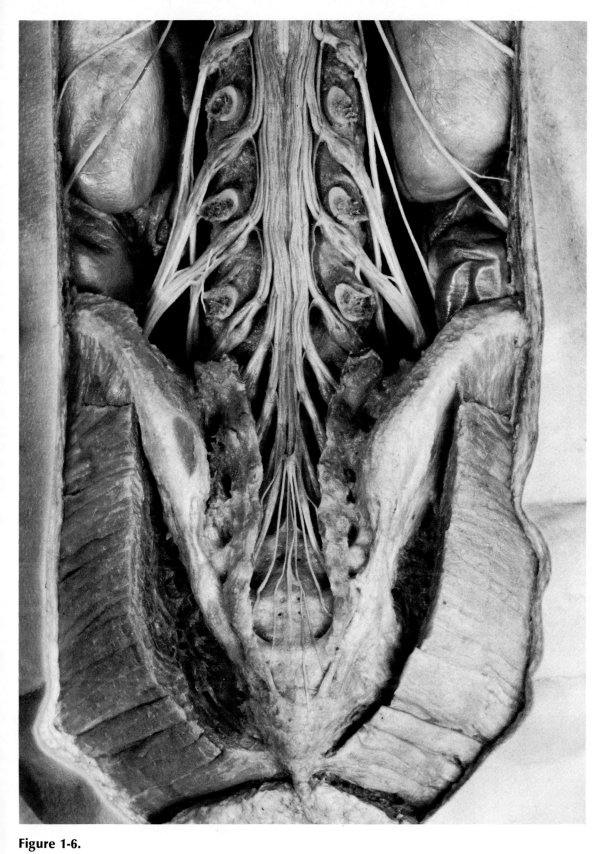

Figure 1-6.

1-7 Dorsal view of membranes of the spinal cord of an adult, with origins of spinal nerves and ganglia

The arches and processes of three thoracic vertebrae (6th–8th) have been removed to display a portion of the spinal cord. The mode of origin of the spinal nerve roots from a number of rootlets is shown, together with associated ganglia and the investing membranes of the spinal cord. The spinal nerves make their exit from the vertebral canal by passing through intervertebral foramina. Note the denticulate ligaments as they pass between the ventral and dorsal roots of the spinal nerve to be attached to the inner surface of the dura mater. In the upper part of the preparation, the pia mater has been stripped away to expose the tracts (gracilis and cuneatus) of each posterior funiculus, which are separated from each other by the dorsal (posterior) median sulcus and dorsal (posterior) intermediate sulci. A little lower down, blood vessels can be seen ramifying in the pia mater.

The spinous process and part of the arch of the 9th thoracic vertebra have been removed to show the fatty tissue and venous plexus of the epidural space. The 10th thoracic vertebra has been left intact, together with a part of the ligamentum flavum.

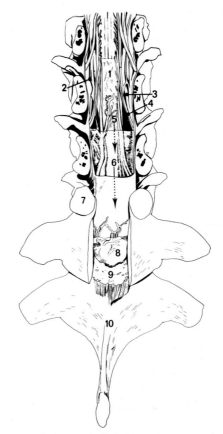

1. Pia mater.
2. Denticulate ligament.
3. Motor root of 7th thoracic nerve.
4. Sensory root of 7th thoracic nerve.
5. Subarachnoid space.
6. Subdural space.
7. Superior articular process of 9th thoracic vertebra.
8. Epidural fat with internal vertebral venous plexus.
9. Ligamentum flavum.
10. 10th thoracic vertebra.

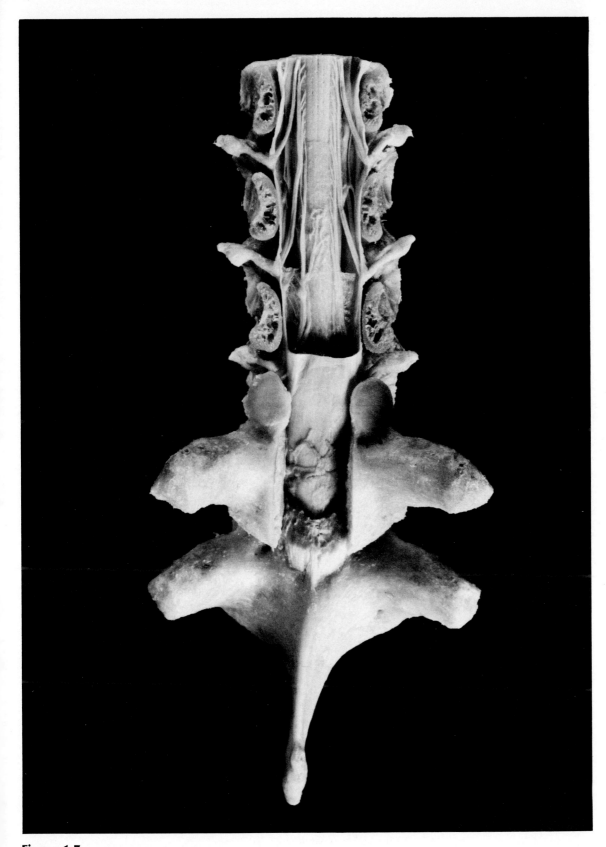

Figure 1-7.

1-8 Transverse section through the spinal cord and vertebral canal, between C2 and C3 vertebrae

The cut surface of the cervical spinal cord is slightly flattened (on both anterior and posterior aspects). In this unstained preparation the gray matter of the cord is not easily recognized. The epidural, subdural, and subarachnoidal spaces are seen, the last-named being a wide interval that in life is filled by cerebrospinal fluid, and continuous at the foramen magnum with the cranial subarachnoid space. In the subarachnoid space, note in particular the dorsal spinal nerve roots (the ventral roots are not seen) and the denticulate ligaments. The spinal ganglia of the 3rd cervical nerves are large, and they are lodged in the intervertebral foramina. Immediately anterior to the spinal ganglion are the vertebral artery and accompanying veins, which ascend and descend through the transverse foramina. Two large venous spaces are seen between the posterior longitudinal ligament and the dura mater. These channels communicate with the internal vertebral venous plexus.

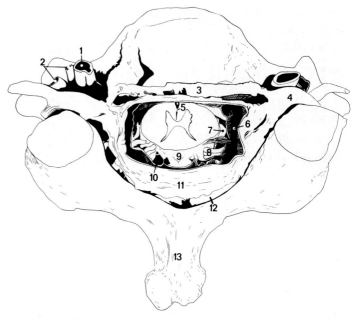

1. Vertebral artery.
2. Vertebral veins.
3. Posterior longitudinal ligament.
4. 3rd cervical spinal ganglion.
5. Ventral (anterior) median fissure with anterior spinal artery.
6. Subdural space.
7. Denticulate ligament.
8. Dorsal rootlets of 3rd cervical nerve.
9. Subarachnoidal trabeculae.
10. Arachnoid mater.
11. Dura mater.
12. Epidural fat.
13. Spinous process of 3rd cervical vertebra.

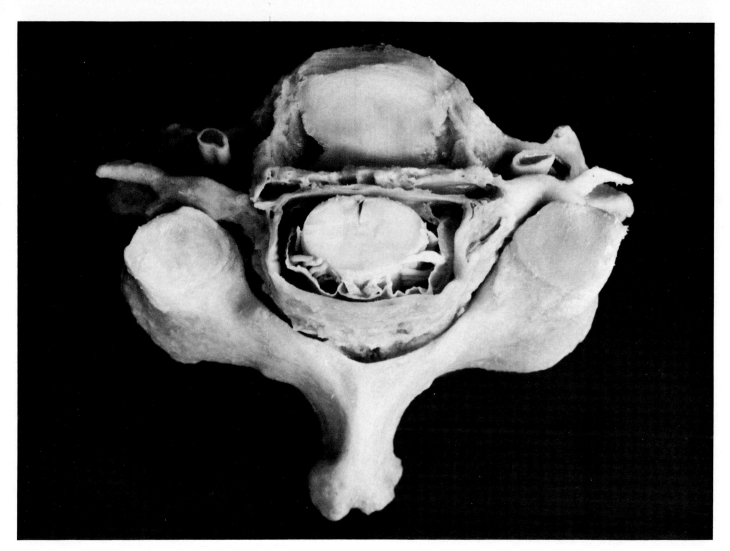

Figure 1-8.

1-9 Transverse sections of spinal cord at different levels: A. Cervical region, B. Thoracic region, C. Lumbar region, D. Sacral region. Note that the myelin stain used has made the white matter appear dark gray or black.

The white matter of the spinal cord is arranged around the gray matter in posterior, lateral, and anterior columns which become progressively smaller from above downwards. In transverse sections, the gray matter is shaped somewhat like a butterfly, although the main portions of gray matter are referred to as the dorsal and ventral columns or horns. The central canal is extremely small and is located within the central gray substance.

In the middle and lower **cervical** region the dorsal gray horns are long, fusiform and pointed posteriorly, whereas the ventral ones are broad and stumpy. Ventral as well as dorsal horns are slender in the **thoracic** region, and the lateral horn, containing the preganglionic neurons of the sympathetic nervous system, is usually discernible. Voluminous and rounded ventral horns characterize transverse sections through the **lumbar** region, and the dorsal horns are larger than at higher levels. When compared to other sections, the gray matter in the **sacral** region occupies the greatest proportion of the total area and the white matter has dwindled to a very small peripheral layer.

Differences in the section profiles also facilitate recognition of the level, cervical sections being both wide and large, thoracic sections smaller and oval-to-circular, lumbar sections circular and much larger than sacral sections. The reticular formation occupies the concavity between dorsal and ventral gray horns and is most distinct in the cervical cord section, although a trace is present also in the section of the thoracic cord.

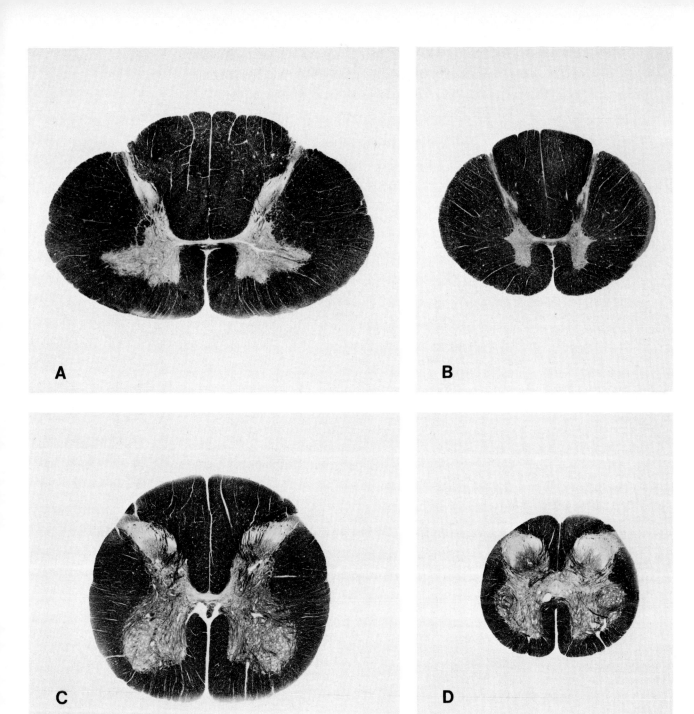

Figure 1-9.

1-10 Transverse section of the spinal cord at midthoracic level, showing approximate positions of the main tracts

The gray matter of the spinal cord is composed of the somata of neurons plus an intricate lattice of nerve processes, and supporting cells or neuroglia. It is formed by symmetrical right and left comma-shaped gray masses connected by the intermediate gray substance, and the entire profile of gray matter resembles a butterfly or letter H. The gray central substance is pierced by the central canal, which is not always visible to the unaided eye. After 40 years of age, its lumen is commonly obliterated. The ventral gray horn is separated from the surface of the spinal cord by the lateral portion of the anterior funiculus. The dorsal gray horn receives incoming or afferent fibers. It is narrow and pointed, and extends almost to the surface of the spinal cord. A cap of pale and almost translucent nervous tissue, the substantia gelatinosa, covers the apex of the posterior gray column. A small, angular, lateral gray column is located adjacent to the lateral white funiculus, and this collection of preganglionic sympathetic neurons can be found at all levels between the 1st thoracic and the 1st lumbar segment of the cord. Nerve cell groups in the gray horns are generally arranged in elongated groups or columns, but in most cases they are not easily identifiable without using special staining techniques.

The white matter of the cord consists mainly of longitudinally running nerve fiber tracts that are arranged in anterior, lateral, and posterior funiculi. It must be emphasized that delineation of the various ascending, descending, and intersegmental tracts as presented in this illustration is both approximate and simplified. Some fiber tracts extensively overlap each other. The fibers of some tracts are widely dispersed (the anterior spinothalamic tract being a good example) whereas others are relatively compact and discrete. At different spinal cord levels and in different species, tracts vary in their relative positions.

1. Dorsal (posterior) median sulcus.
2. Dorsal (posterior) intermediate sulcus.
3. Posterior median septum.
4. Posterior funiculus.
5. Posterior lateral sulcus.
6. Substantia gelatinosa.
7. Dorsal (posterior) gray column, nucleus proprius.
8. Lateral funiculus.
9. Thoracic nucleus.
10. Intermediolateral gray column.
11. Ventral (anterior) gray column.
12. Ventral funiculus.
13. Anterior median fissure.
14. Ventral white commissure.
15. Intermediate gray substance.
16. Medial longitudinal fascicle.
17. Anterior corticospinal tract.
18. Anterior tectospinal tract.
19. Reticulospinal tract.
20. Vestibulospinal tract.
21. Spinotectal tract.
22. Anterior spinocerebellar tract.
23. Rubrospinal tract.
24. Lateral spinothalamic tract.
25. Lateral corticospinal tract.
26. Posterior spinocerebellar tract.
27. Cuneate fascicle.
28. Gracile fascicle.

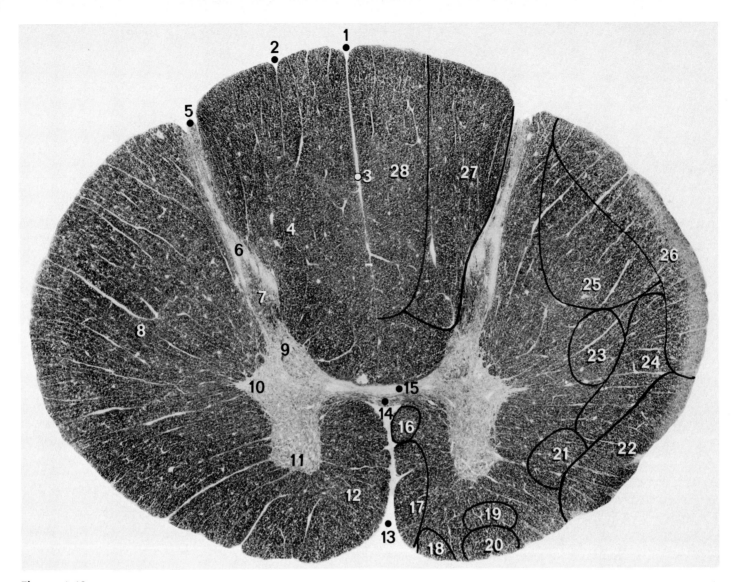

Figure 1-10.

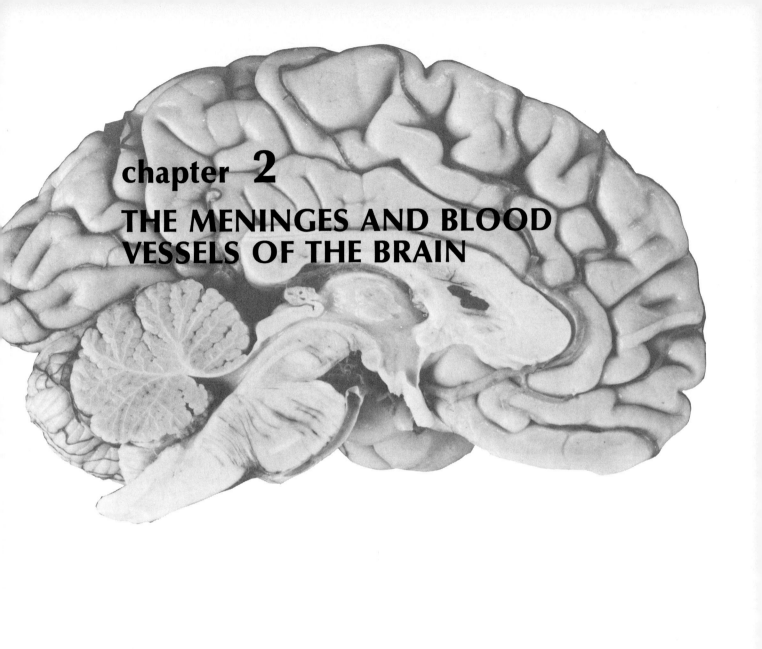

chapter 2
THE MENINGES AND BLOOD VESSELS OF THE BRAIN

The outer surface of the **cerebral** dura mater is rough, especially where its outer, endosteal layer adheres to the circumference of the foramen magnum. The tough and dense tube of dura mater that loosely envelops the spinal cord extends from the foramen magnum to its blind ending at the level of the 2nd sacral vertebra, widening in two locations to accommodate the cervical and lumbar enlargements of the spinal cord.

The smooth outer surface of the **spinal** dura is accounted for by the absence of an outer, endosteal layer. On each side the spinal roots, ganglia, and proximal portions of the spinal nerves are enveloped by tubular extensions of the spinal dura. This preparation illustrates how the entire central nervous system is enclosed in a continuous dural investment.

It is attached above to the rim of the foramen magnum and to the bodies of the 2nd and 3rd cervical vertebrae. The thread of pia mater known as the filum terminale penetrates the lower end of the dural tube and anchors it to the posterior aspect of the coccyx.

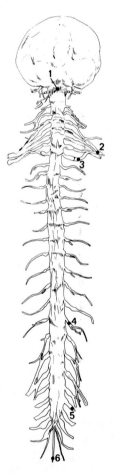

1. Foramen magnum level.
2. Brachial plexus.
3. 1st thoracic nerve.
4. 1st lumbar spinal ganglion.
5. 1st sacral nerve.
6. Filum terminale.

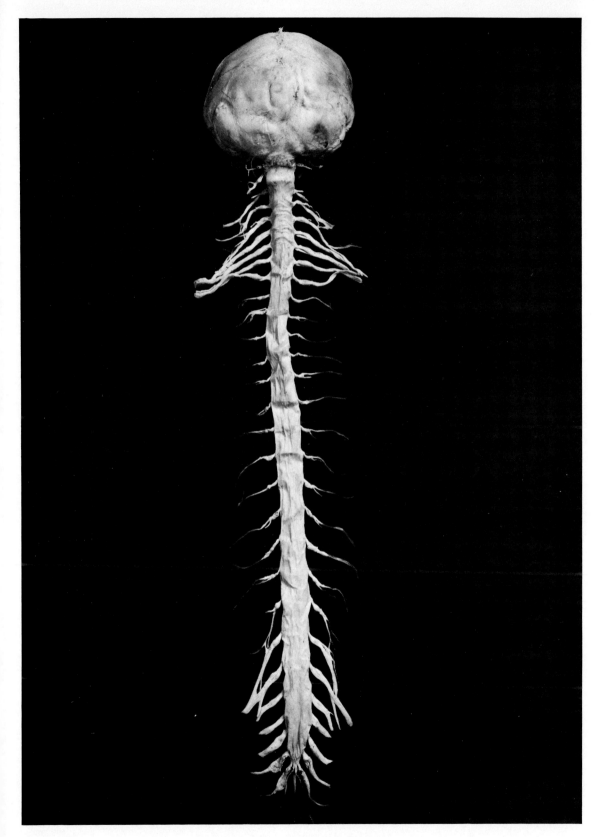

Figure 2-1.

2-2 Cerebral dura mater, with the superior sagittal venous sinus and its lateral lacunae opened to show the arachnoid granulations

The cerebral dura mater which encloses the brain has been detached carefully from the internal surfaces of the cranial bones. Because the outer, endosteal layer of the dura was firmly adherent to the bone, the outer surface of the dura has a rough appearance (indicating the difficulty experienced in separating dense dural connective tissue from bone). A pattern of dark lines produced by branches of the middle meningeal artery and vein is seen on both sides of the specimen, these vessels being enclosed within the outer, endosteal layer of the dura.

The superior sagittal venous sinus has been opened together with its lateral lacunae, and this has exposed arachnoid granulations. Many openings in the walls of the superior sagittal sinus and in its lateral lacunae mark the sites of entry of superior cerebral veins into the superior sagittal sinus. Note how widely the lateral lacunae spread out in both parietal regions, and the relatively small extent of other portions of the lateral lacunae.

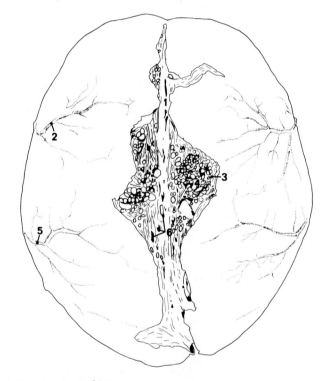

1. Superior sagittal sinus.
2. Frontal branch of middle meningeal artery.
3. Lateral venous lacuna.
4. Arachnoid granulations.
5. Parietal branch of middle meningeal artery.
6. Openings of superior cerebral veins into superior sagittal sinus.

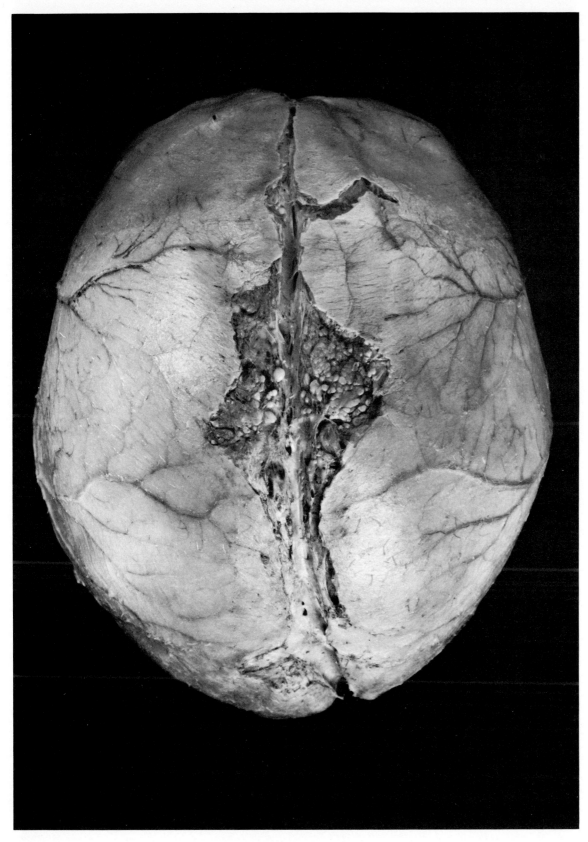

Figure 2-2.

Arachnoid granulations in lateral lacunae of the superior sagittal sinus: closeup view

The arachnoid granulations are bulblike protrusions that show considerable variations in size (enlarging with age). Mostly arranged in clusters, they project principally into the lateral lacunae that are connected with the superior sagittal sinus. A coexisting microscopic form of arachnoid projections (arachnoid villi) cannot be seen, but, on close inspection, a complex network of white collagen strands belonging to the internal meningeal layer of the dura is visible. The arachnoid granulations protrude between the trabeculae into the superior sagittal sinus and its lacunae. The granulations and trabeculae are covered by a smooth endothelium, and the intertrabecular spaces that are not occupied by granulations are usually the sites of junctions between the superior cerebral veins and the sinus or one of its lacunae. The intimate relationship that exists between arachnoid granulations (and villi) and the venous blood of the sinus emphasizes the crucial function of the granulations in transferring cerebral spinal fluid back into the blood stream.

1. Superior sagittal sinus.
2. Arachnoid granulations.
3. Openings of superior cerebral veins into superior sagittal sinus.

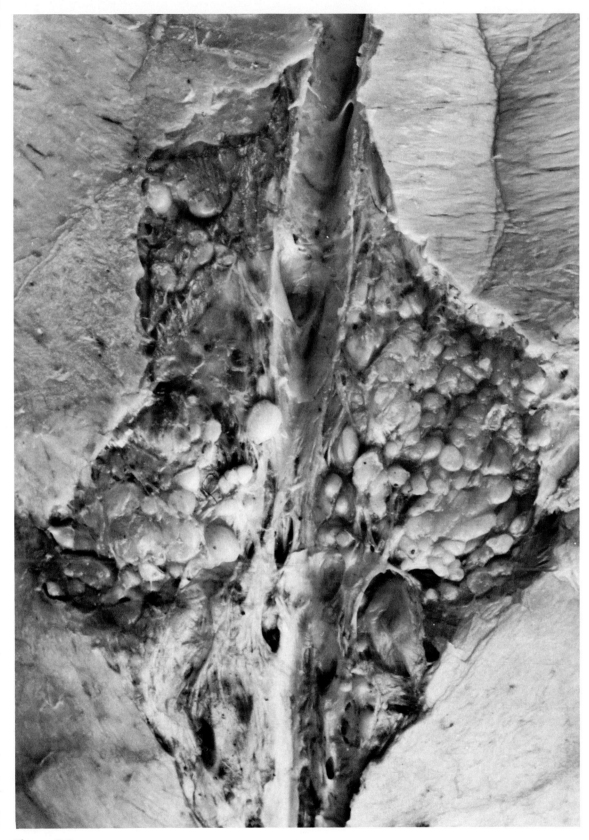

Figure 2-3.

Brain in its covering of dura mater, with branches of the middle meningeal artery: lateral view

The strong fibrous membrane that covers the brain is the cerebral dura mater. Its outer or endosteal layer has been detached from the cranial bones. Its inner or meningeal layer provides direct support for the brain. The outer surface of the dura is rough because many fibrous attachments to the skull have been torn across during preparation. The outer dura is most firmly attached along suture lines and around all foramina of the cranium. Embedded within the dense connective tissue of the outer dural layer are two major branches of the middle meningeal artery which make numerous anastomoses and supply the dura mater and the inner table of the cranial bones. Some very slender veins can be distinguished from their accompanying arteries by the darker coloration of the former. Outside the main skull cavity, dural sheaths cover the optic nerves and the meningeal layer of dura is continuous with the sclera of the eyeball. Emerging from the middle part of the dural sac are the maxillary and mandibular divisions of the trigeminal nerve, and more posteriorly the hypoglossal and some spinal nerves are shown. Outside the skull the dura fuses with the epineurium of these nerves. At the level of the foramen magnum the cerebral dura mater is continuous with the spinal dura mater.

1. Frontal ramus of middle meningeal artery.
2. Parietal ramus of middle meningeal artery.
3. Eyeball.
4. Optic nerve.
5. Maxillary division of trigeminal nerve.
6. Hypoglossal nerve.
7. Mandibular division of trigeminal nerve.

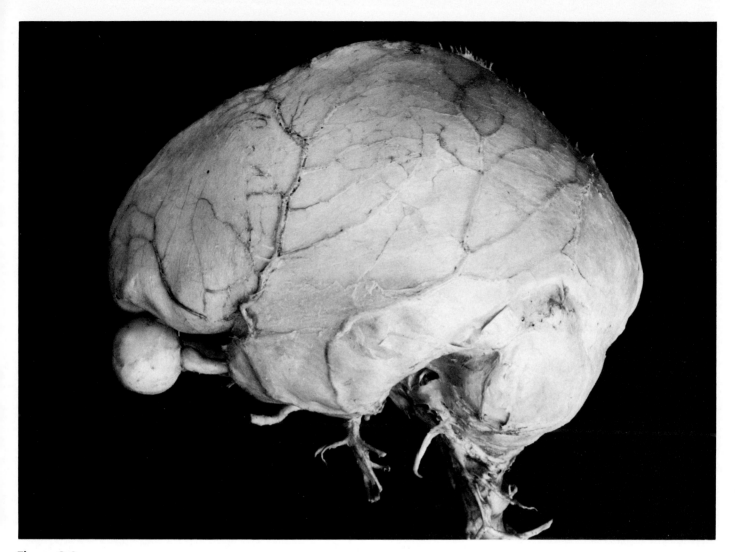

Figure 2-4.

To display structures on the basal aspect of the brain with their coverings of dura, the outer, endosteal layer of dura mater has been detached from the base of the skull. Near the front of the brain, in the midline, a deep sagittal groove in the dura indicates the site where the crista galli of the ethmoid bone was accommodated. On each side of the groove the dura is rough, because of its attachment to the cribriform plate of the ethmoid bone and because it is pierced by numerous olfactory nerve bundles.

Somewhat further back, the dura has been separated from the body of the sphenoid bone. Near the midline, dura covers the optic chiasma and the pituitary gland; more laterally, it provides a strong medial wall for the cavernous sinus. The endosteal dura that invests the optic chiasma can be traced from the chiasma along the optic nerve to the site at which the outer layer of the dura was cut at the entrance of the orbit. More anteriorly, the optic nerve is surrounded only by the smooth meningeal or inner layer of the dura, which blends with the sclera of the eyeball.

Note the internal carotid artery entering the cavernous sinus. The cut ends of the nerves that pass through the cavernous sinus are seen in the neighborhood of the optic nerve. By tracing the maxillary and mandibular divisions of the trigeminal nerve backwards, the swelling that contains the trigeminal ganglion can be located. Lateral to the foregoing structures, two major branches of the middle meningeal artery produce sinuous ridges in the dura. Behind the temporal regions, note the two wide and deep grooves which outline the petrous parts of the temporal bones. On the left side of the illustration the vestibulocochlear and facial nerves can be seen. The cerebral dura mater is continued without interruption as the tube of dura that invests the spinal cord. The level of emergence of the 1st cervical nerve or of the foramen magnum is the anatomic landmark for the transition. The spinal dura lacks an outer, endosteal layer. Note the ventral and dorsal rami of cervical spinal nerves. (The 2nd spinal nerve on the left side of the illustration is not present.)

1. Optic nerve.
2. Dura concealing the optic chiasma.
3. Dura concealing the hypophysis (pituitary gland).
4. Maxillary division of trigeminal nerve.
5. Internal carotid artery in cavernous sinus.
6. Mandibular division of trigeminal nerve.
7. Dura concealing the trigeminal ganglion.
8. Middle meningeal artery.
9. Facial nerve.
10. Vestibulocochlear nerve.
11. Hypoglossal nerve.
12. 1st cervical nerve.
13. Motor root of 2nd cervical nerve.

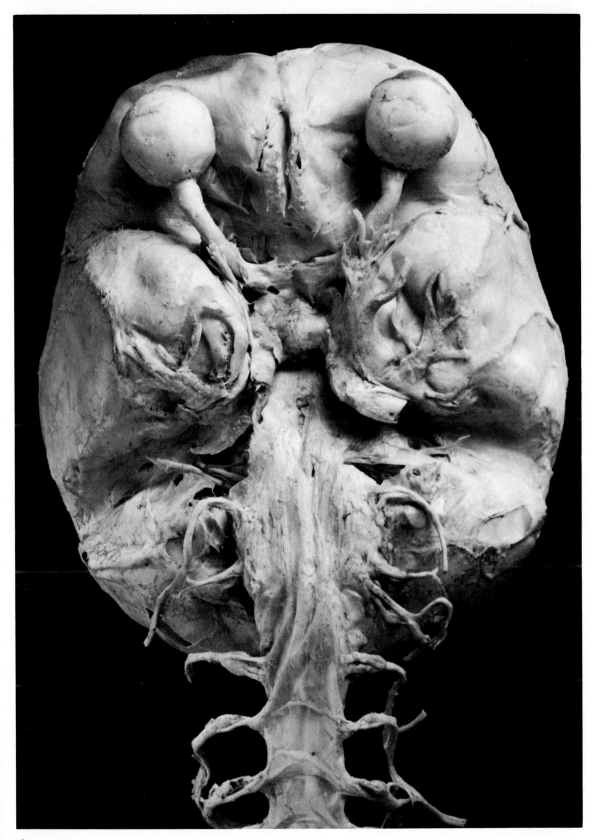

Figure 2-5.

The falx cerebri is a two-layered, sickle-shaped dural septum, which descends from the skull vault into the longitudinal cerebral fissure. One of the two layers is seen covering the medial surface of the left cerebral hemisphere. Anteroinferiorly, the falx is narrow and attached firmly to the crista galli of the ethmoid bone. The posterior part of the falx cerebri is broader and is attached in the median plane to the superior surface of the tentorium cerebelli, a sloping fold of the dura that overlies the cerebellum like a tent. Along its upper margin the two layers of the falx separate, to enclose the superior sagittal sinus. In the specimen this sinus is opened, exposing openings of superior cerebral veins and clusters of arachnoid granulations. The free, concave lower margin of the falx cerebri encloses the inferior sagittal sinus. The straight sinus, located at the site of attachment of the falx cerebri to the tentorium cerebelli, has been opened. The straight sinus, formed by the union of the inferior sagittal sinus and the great cerebral vein, is enclosed jointly by the falx cerebri and tentorium cerebelli at their site of attachment. The great cerebral vein can be seen curving below the splenium of the corpus callosum to help form the straight sinus.

The cerebellomedullary cistern is the largest of the spaces (containing cerebrospinal fluid) between the arachnoid mater and the pia mater, and is located between the cerebellum and the medulla oblongata. It continues downwards without interruption into the subarachnoid space surrounding the spinal cord, and upwards and laterally into the subarachnoid space of the posterior cranial fossa. The cistern is traversed by delicate connective tissue trabeculae, which bridge across the interval between the arachnoid mater and the pia mater. The shallow pontine cistern on the ventral surface of the pons lodges the basilar artery and is continuous anterosuperiorly with the interpeduncular cistern. The hypophysis or pituitary gland has been bisected in the sagittal plane. The infundibulum of the hypophysis (which connects the hypothalamus to the pituitary) pierces the diaphragma sellae, a fold of dura mater that roofs over the hypophyseal fossa.

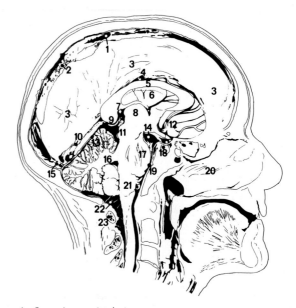

1. Superior sagittal sinus.
2. Arachnoid granulations.
3. Falx cerebri.
4. Inferior sagittal sinus.
5. Corpus callosum.
6. Septum pellucidum.
7. Tela choroidea of 3rd ventricle.
8. Thalamus.
9. Great cerebral vein.
10. Straight sinus of tentorium cerebelli.
11. Tectum of midbrain.
12. Anterior cerebral artery.
13. Tentorium cerebelli.
14. Interpeduncular cistern.
15. Confluence of sinuses.
16. Superior cerebellar peduncle.
17. Pons.
18. Pituitary gland.
19. Pontine cistern.
20. Nasal septum.
21. Medulla oblongata.
22. Cerebello-medullary cistern.
23. Posterior arch of atlas.

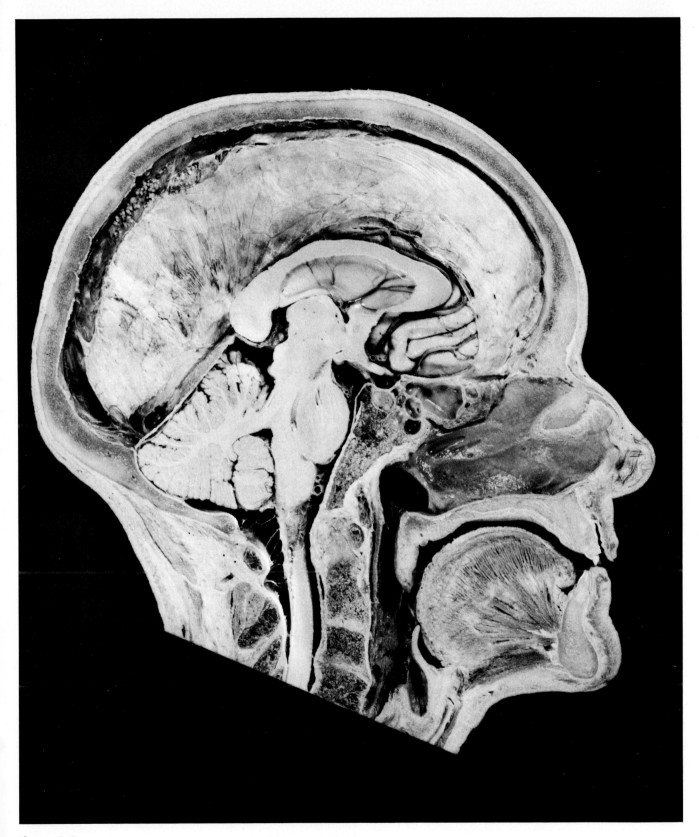

Figure 2-6.

On the superolateral surfaces of both cerebral hemispheres, the arachnoid mater appears as a delicate, transparent membrane through which the contours of the cerebral gyri can be seen quite readily, together with the venous and arterial channels that traverse the subarachnoid space. Except at the site of the stem of the lateral sulcus, the meningeal arachnoid does not accompany the pia mater into the cerebral sulci, but instead bridges across them so that pia and arachnoid are in contact only on the summits of the gyri. The **arteries** on the brain surface possess thicker walls, are more deeply placed in the sulci, and tend to be more sinuous (particularly with advancing age) than the cerebral **veins**. Some of the larger veins have been cut across at their sites of entry into the superior sagittal sinus. Note the clusters of arachnoid granulations along the margins of the longitudinal cerebral fissure: these are concentrated mainly in the parietal regions.

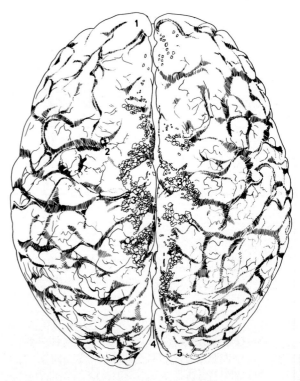

1. Frontal pole of cerebral hemisphere.
2. Site of entry of superior cerebral vein into superior sagittal sinus.
3. Arachnoid granulations.
4. Longitudinal cerebral fissure.
5. Occipital pole of cerebral hemisphere.

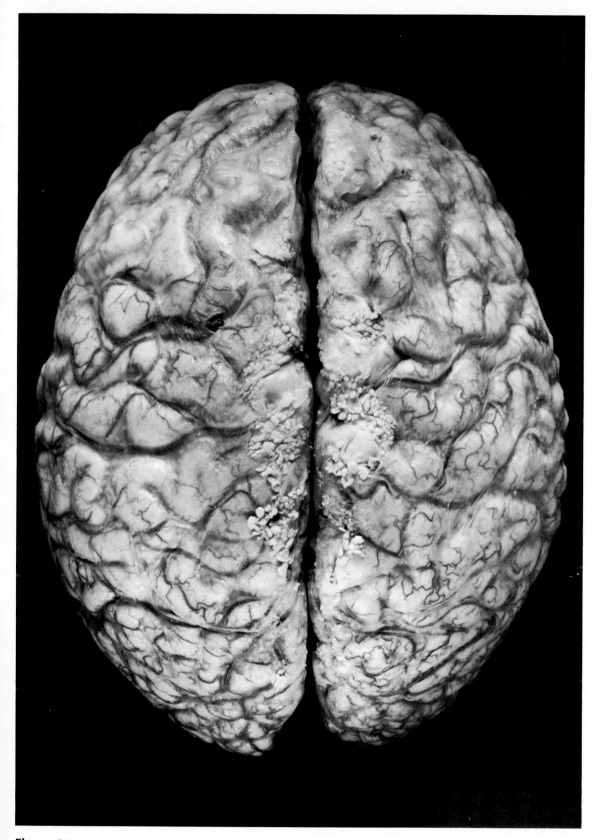

Figure 2-7.

2-8 Vessels of the superolateral surface of the left hemisphere, seen through the arachnoid mater

The arachnoid mater is a semitransparent and extremely delicate membrane separated from the dura mater by a capillary interval, the subdural space. Through it, the cerebral gyri and numerous blood vessels are clearly recognizable in the subarachnoid space. The arachnoid is pushed (by the lesser wing of the sphenoid bone) into the stem of the lateral sulcus.

Elsewhere on the superolateral surface, the arachnoid bridges across the sulci. The arachnoid covers the superficial middle cerebral vein, which passes through the lateral sulcus, receiving numerous tributaries. The branches of the middle cerebral artery are more rounded, more deeply placed and of smaller caliber than the veins. On the portion of the cerebellum that is shown, numerous veins and arteries occupy the subarachnoid space.

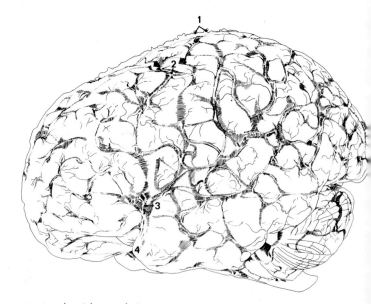

1. Arachnoid granulations.
2. Superior anastomotic vein.
3. Superficial middle cerebral vein.
4. Temporal pole of cerebral hemisphere.

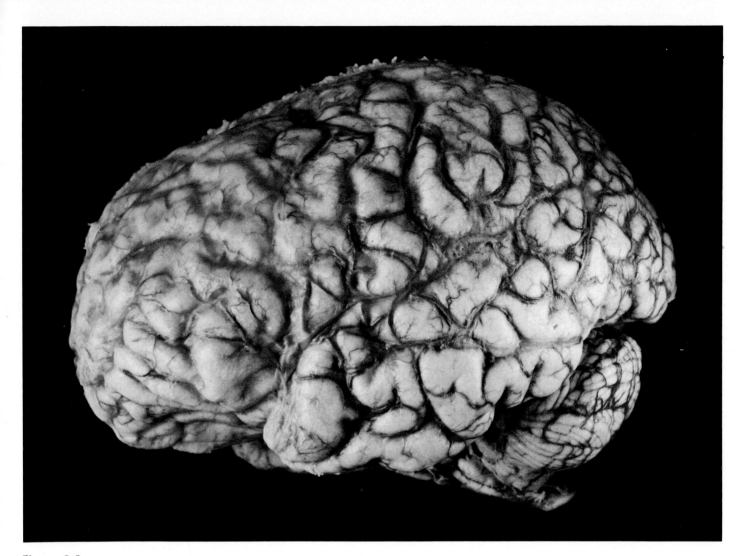

Figure 2-8.

Subarachnoid cisterns at the base of the brain

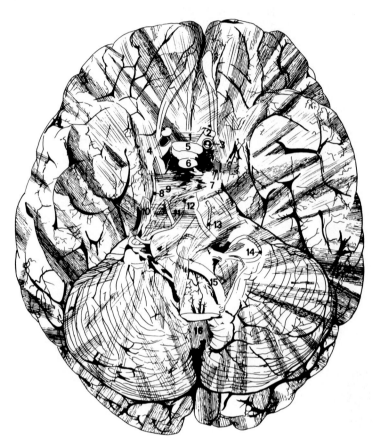

At certain specific points on the base of the brain, the subarachnoid space is much wider than elsewhere. Some of these wide intervals between the arachnoid and the pia mater—the subarachnoid cisterns—can be seen. In particular, note the voluminous cerebellomedullary subarachnoid cistern (cisterna magna). The pontine cistern located on the ventral aspects of the pons is also large, and contains the basilar artery and some of its branches. In this preparation, numerous stretched strands of connective tissue belonging to the arachnoid mater can be distinguished between the two temporal lobes. The circulus arteriosus (of Willis) lies within the large interpeduncular cistern, which is continuous rostrally with the chiasmatic cistern, and envelops the optic chiasma. The pituitary gland itself is not surrounded by arachnoid, but a white membrane provides it with a dural covering, part of which dips in to connect with the anterior and posterior lobes. The chiasmatic cistern is continuous laterally with the cistern of the lateral fossa, which bridges across the lateral fissure and accommodates the middle cerebral artery. The arachnoid mater is carried by the lesser wing of the sphenoid bone into the stem of the lateral fissure.

1. Chiasmatic cistern.
2. Optic nerve.
3. Internal carotid artery.
4. Cistern of middle cerebral artery.
5. Anterior lobe of pituitary gland.
6. Posterior lobe of pituitary gland.
7. Oculomotor nerve.
8. Trochlear nerve.
9. Interpeduncular cistern.
10. Trigeminal nerve.
11. Pontine cistern.
12. Basilar artery.
13. Abducent nerve.
14. Inferior posterior cerebellar artery.
15. Left vertebral artery.
16. Cerebellomedullary cistern.

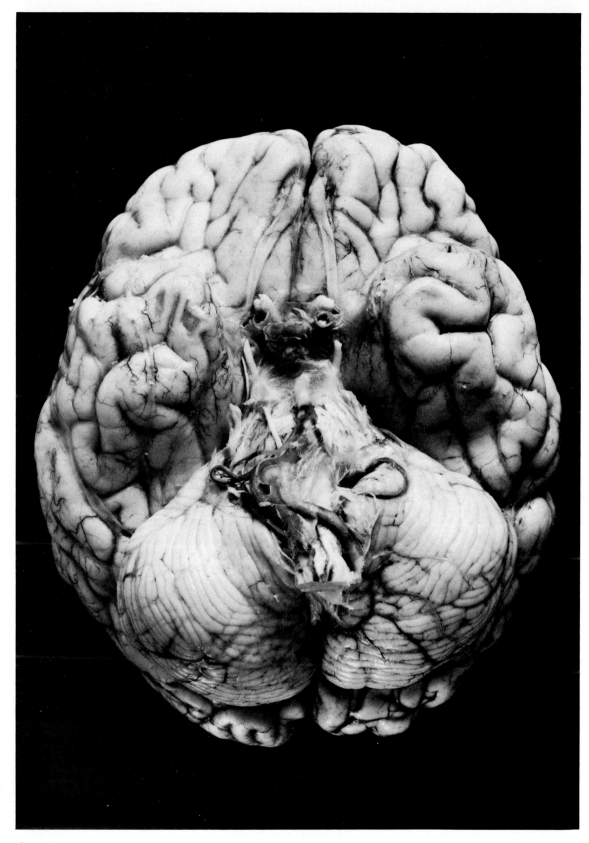

Figure 2-9.

The arterial circle surrounds the optic chiasma and lies mainly in the interpeduncular cistern. The anterior communicating artery links together the two anterior cerebral arteries. Each middle cerebral artery is very large and has the appearance of being a direct continuation of the internal carotid artery. The oculomotor nerve passes between the posterior cerebral and superior cerebellar arteries.

A central system of arterial branches penetrates the surface to supply deep structures of the brain, including the basal nuclei. The majority of these enter the brain through the anterior and posterior perforating substance, and they do not anastomose with one another. The cortical system of arterial branches ramifies over the cerebrum to supply the cortex with arterioles that can anastomose in the pia mater.

The posterior inferior cerebellar artery arises from the vertebral artery and is its largest branch. It pursues a course on the side of the upper part of the medulla oblongata, giving branches to the medulla, the posterior part of the inferior cerebellar surface, and the inferior vermis. On each side, the anterior spinal artery is a branch of the vertebral artery. The origins of the anterior spinal arteries are not seen in this preparation, but their common trunk can be traced down the ventral (anterior) median fissure of the medulla oblongata and the 1st segment of the spinal cord.

The basilar artery, formed at the lower border of the pons by the union of the two vertebral arteries, is large and in this preparation occupies the midline groove on the ventral aspect of the pons, to which it supplies numerous slender pontine branches. Other branches that spring from the basilar artery are the labyrinthine or internal auditory, the anterior inferior cerebellar, and the relatively large superior cerebellar artery.

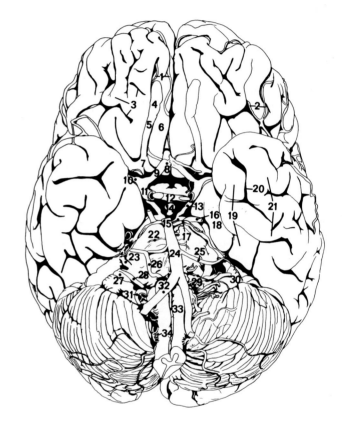

1. Orbital branches of anterior cerebral artery.
2. Orbital branches of middle cerebral artery.
3. Orbital sulci and gyri.
4. Olfactory bulb.
5. Olfactory tract.
6. Straight gyrus.
7. Olfactory trigone.
8. Anterior communicating artery.
9. Anterior cerebral artery.
10. Middle cerebral artery.
11. Internal carotid artery.
12. Optic chiasma.
13. Posterior communicating artery.
14. Infundibulum.
15. Posterior cerebral artery.
16. Oculomotor nerve.
17. Superior cerebellar artery.
18. Parahippocampal gyrus.
19. Medial occipitotemporal gyrus.
20. Occipitotemporal sulcus.
21. Lateral occipitotemporal gyrus.
22. Pontine branch of basilar artery.
23. Trigeminal nerve.
24. Basilar artery.
25. Labyrinthine artery.
26. Abducent nerve.
27. Vestibulocochlear nerve.
28. Facial nerve.
29. Anterior inferior cerebellar artery.
30. Flocculus.
31. Posterior inferior cerebellar artery.
32. Right vertebral artery.
33. Anterior spinal artery.
34. Ventral rootlets of 1st cervical nerve.

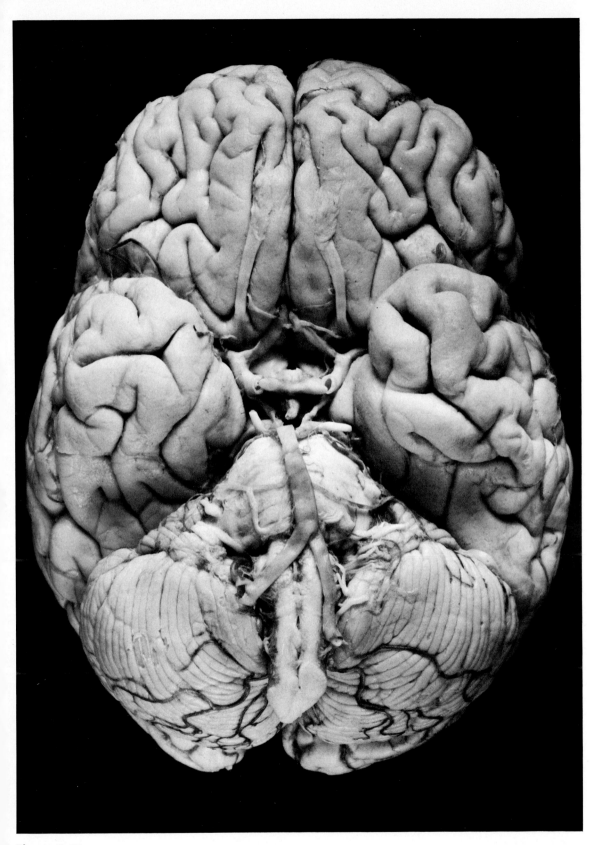

Figure 2-10.

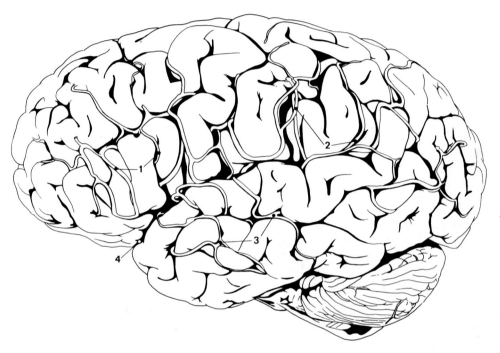

The middle cerebral vessels run in the stem of the lateral sulcus, and branches of the artery emerge from the stem and three (horizontal anterior, ascending anterior and posterior) rami of the lateral sulcus; the branches run in all directions over the superolateral surface of the hemisphere. The main trunk of the middle cerebral artery cannot be seen in this preparation because it is located deep inside the lateral sulcus near the surface of the insula. Orbital branches pass on to the inferior orbital surface of the hemisphere where they anastomose with orbital branches of the anterior cerebral artery. Small branches of the anterior and posterior cerebral arteries extend from the superomedial margin of the hemisphere to supply the adjoining portion of the superolateral surface. Frontal and parietal branches of the middle cerebral artery meet up and anastomose with some of these offshoots from the anterior and posterior cerebral arteries. At the lower margin of the temporal lobe, vessels derived from the middle cerebral artery anastomose with temporal branches of the posterior cerebral artery. The middle cerebral artery supplies very important cortical areas, including motor, premotor, sensory, auditory and wide association regions of the cerebral cortex.

1. Frontal rami of middle cerebral artery.
2. Parietal rami of middle cerebral artery.
3. Anterior and posterior temporal rami of middle cerebral artery.
4. Lateral sulcus of cerebral hemisphere.

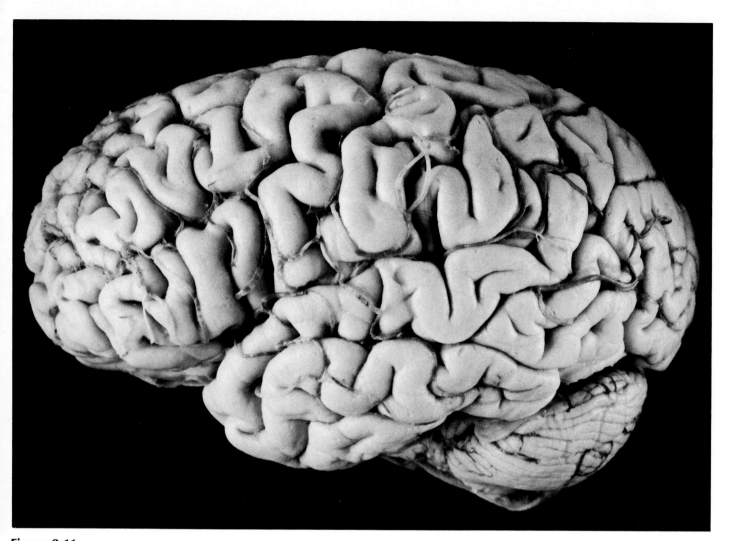

Figure 2-11.

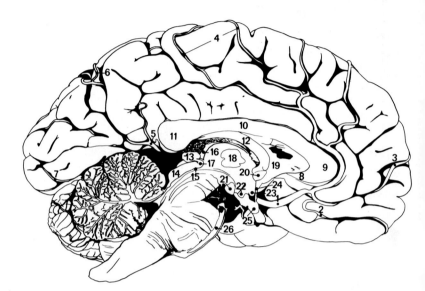

The final segment of the left vertebral artery is seen at the lower border of the pons, close to the union with its fellow where the two vessels form the basilar artery. After giving off pontine and other branches, it divides at the upper border of the pons into two posterior cerebral arteries. Springing from the latter are branches that supply the medial surface of the occipital lobe. Other branches assist in supplying the superolateral and inferior surfaces of the hemisphere. Note the parieto-occipital and calcarine branches, the latter being of great importance because it supplies primary visual cortex.

The anterior cerebral artery can be seen running on the medial surface of the hemisphere, first beneath and then around the genu of the corpus callosum. Its branches are cortical and central (the latter supplying structures in the interior of the brain). Some of its frontal branches ramify on the medial surface of the frontal lobe; others pass to the inferior surface as orbital branches, and anastomose with orbital branches of the middle cerebral artery. Both frontal and parietal branches of the anterior cerebral artery traverse the cingulate sulcus and the surface of the medial frontal gyrus, and terminal twigs supply a strip on the adjoining part of the superolateral surface of the hemisphere. After giving off the branches described above, the anterior cerebral artery continues backwards deep in the callosal sulcus as an artery of greatly diminished caliber. The distribution of the branches of the anterior cerebral artery can be examined by using arteriograms of the internal carotid artery.

Many arterial branches arise from the vertebral and basilar artery to supply the medulla oblongata and the pons. In addition, relatively small branches of the posterior cerebral and posterior communicating arteries penetrate the posterior perforated substance to reach the midbrain tegmentum.

1. Anterior cerebral artery.
2. Orbital ramus of anterior cerebral artery.
3. Frontal ramus of anterior cerebral artery.
4. Parietal rami of anterior cerebral artery.
5. Posterior cerebral artery.
6. Parieto-occipital ramus of posterior cerebral artery.
7. Occipital ramus of posterior cerebral artery.
8. Rostrum of corpus callosum.
9. Genu of corpus callosum.
10. Body of corpus callosum.
11. Splenium of corpus callosum.
12. Column of fornix.
13. Pineal body.
14. Tectum of midbrain.
15. Mesencephalic (cerebral) aqueduct.
16. Habenular trigone.
17. Posterior commissure.
18. Interthalamic adhesion.
19. Septum pellucidum.
20. Rostral (anterior) commissure.
21. Mamillary body.
22. Infundibular recess.
23. Optic recess.
24. Lamina terminalis.
25. Optic chiasma.
26. Basilar artery.

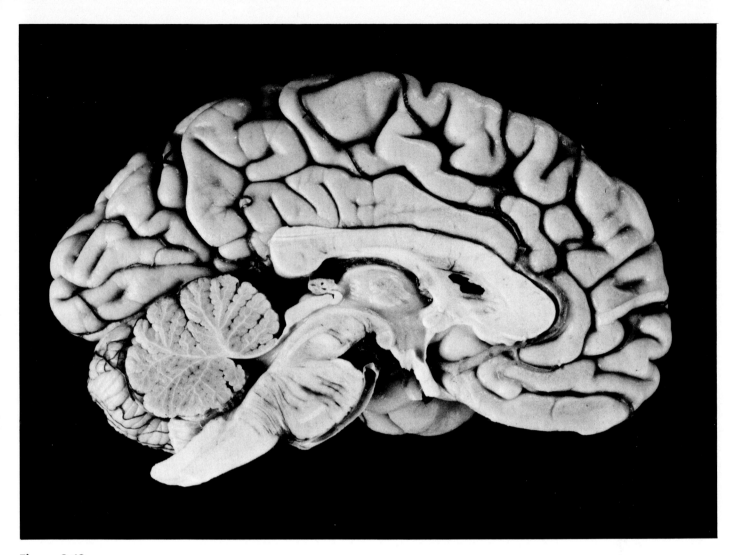

Figure 2-12.

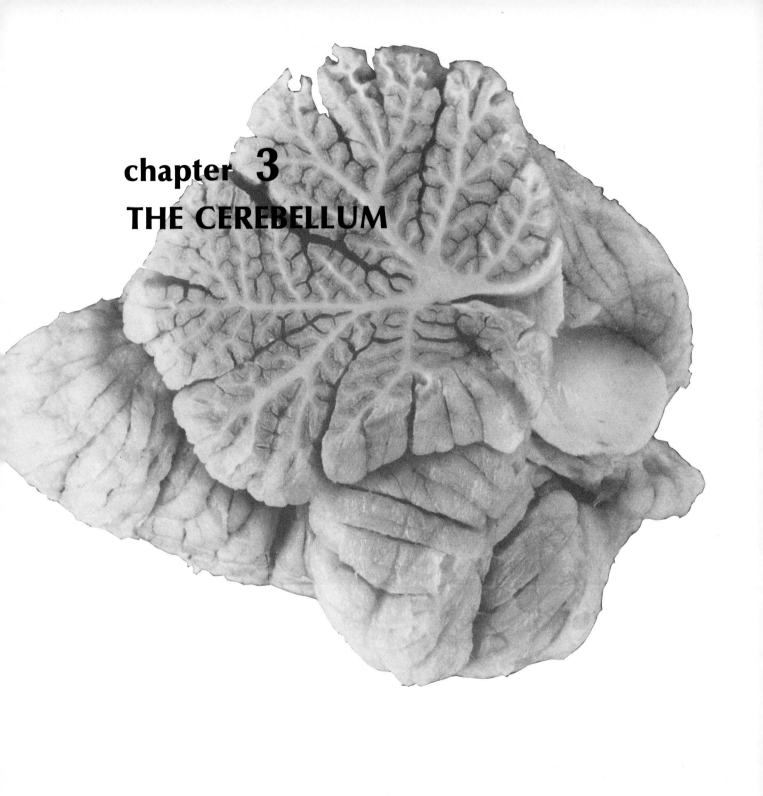

chapter **3**
THE CEREBELLUM

Superior surface of the cerebellum

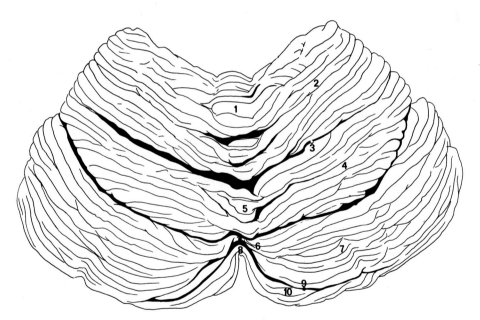

Laterally, the two large masses are the cerebellar hemispheres, joined to each other by the narrow median vermis. Very distinctive are the laminations of the cerebellar cortex. Mainly parallel fissures and sulci are interposed between the thin, transversely running folia of the cerebellar cortex. The median portion or vermis forms a low ridge from which the lobules of the hemispheres slope gently downwards and laterally. The primary fissure is deep and sharply delimits the culmen from the declive of the vermis; then it extends anterolaterally across the superior surface of the hemisphere, separating the quadrangular lobule from the more posterior lobulus simplex. The voluminous superior semilunar lobule occupies the area posterior to the lobulus simplex, while only a thin strip of the inferior semilunar lobule appears at the posterior edge of the surface.

1. Culmen.
2. Quadrangular lobule.
3. Fissura prima.
4. Lobulus simplex.
5. Declive.
6. Folium of vermis.
7. Superior semilunar lobule.
8. Tuber of vermis.
9. Horizontal fissure.
10. Inferior semilunar lobule.

Figure 3-1.

Cerebellum: posterosuperior view

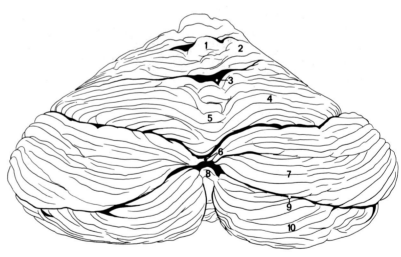

The superior vermis forms the apex or median ridge, and is not clearly demarcated from the corresponding portions of the hemispheres which slope downwards toward the margins. Anteriorly, the culmen of the vermis and the declive behind it are associated respectively with the quadrangular lobule and the lobulus simplex of the cerebellar hemisphere. Note that the two extensive superior semilunar lobules are related across the midline by the diminutive folium of the vermis. Below the latter is the tuber of the vermis, which connects two voluminous inferior semilunar lobules. The deep horizontal fissure intervenes between the superior and inferior semilunar lobules.

1. Culmen.
2. Quadrangular lobule.
3. Fissura prima.
4. Lobulus simplex.
5. Declive.
6. Folium of vermis.
7. Superior semilunar lobule.
8. Tuber of vermis.
9. Horizontal fissure.
10. Inferior semilunar lobule.

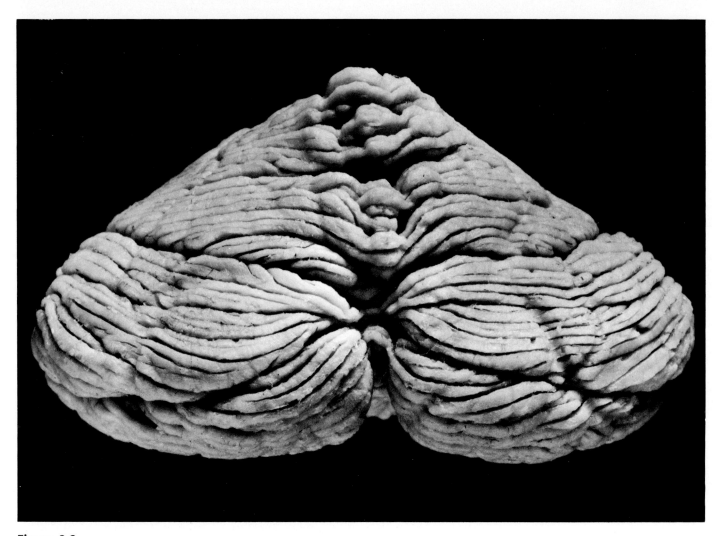

Figure 3-2.

Cerebellum: inferior view

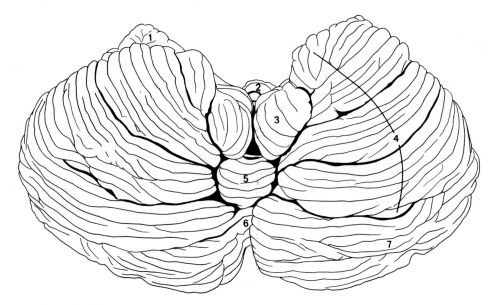

The inferior folia of the vermis project from the floor of a deep hollow known as the vallecula of the cerebellum, which separates the two cerebellar hemispheres. The pyramid of the inferior vermis is a prominent eminence composed of about six folia, in a deep sulcus or furrow which sets it apart from its lateral extensions which are the massive biventral lobules. Posterior to the pyramid, the few folia of the tuber can be seen, flanked by the inferior semilunar lobules. The portion of the vermis immediately anterior to the pyramid, the uvula, is overlapped by the prominent tonsils, which are lobules of hemisphere that are continuous with the uvula across the floor of the vallecula and well separated from the remainder of the inferior surface of the hemisphere. On each side, the cerebellar hemisphere fits into the posterior cranial fossa. (Branches of the anterior inferior and posterior inferior cerebellar arteries, derived from the basilar and vertebral arteries respectively, were lodged in the numerous shallow grooves seen in the surface of the cerebellum.)

1. Flocculus.
2. Uvula of vermis.
3. Tonsil.
4. Biventral lobule.
5. Pyramid of vermis.
6. Tuber of vermis.
7. Inferior semilunar lobule.

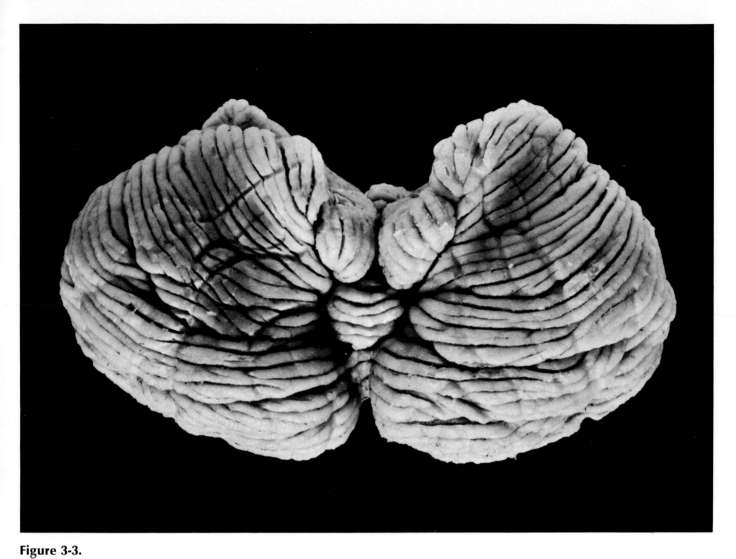

Figure 3-3.

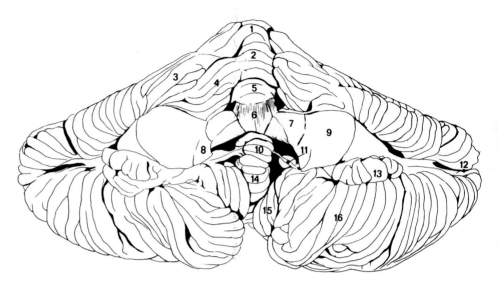

Several parts of the vermis (together with corresponding parts of the hemispheres) are shown, as well as the general arrangement of the cerebellar peduncles. The lingula of the vermis is a rather thick structure, firmly attached to the superior medullary velum. Immediately above the lingula, four or five folia constitute the central lobule of the vermis which is continuous laterally with the ala of the central lobule. In the midline, above the central lobule, is the culmen which projects above the rest of the superior surface of the cerebellum.

Separated from the lingula by a deep, wide fissure—the superior recess of the 4th ventricle—are the folia of the nodulus. Attached to each side of the nodule is a thin, white lamina, the inferior medullary velum. The nodule is connected by the inferior medullary velum to the peduncle of the flocculus and to the flocculus itself, the crenated margin of which protrudes from the remainder of the cerebellum. The lingula and the flocculo-nodular complex are close together topographically and functionally, all of them being archicerebellar and all of them making predominantly vestibular connections.

Below the nodulus and separated from it by the posterolateral fissure is the uvula of the vermis, and the pair of prominent tonsils that partially overlap the uvula. In this preparation the tonsils are somewhat irregular and asymmetric masses of cerebellar cortex.

Lateral to the tonsils lie the large, irregular biventral lobules. Superomedial to each flocculus is the oval profile formed by the cut surfaces of the middle and inferior cerebellar peduncles, which are not clearly demarcated from one another. Most of the fibers in the superior cerebellar peduncle, which is more medially placed, are ascending to gain access to the thalamus and to the red nucleus of the midbrain.

1. Culmen.
2. Central lobule.
3. Quadrangular lobule.
4. Ala of central lobule.
5. Lingula of vermis.
6. Superior medullary velum.
7. Superior cerebellar peduncle.
8. Inferior cerebellar peduncle.
9. Middle cerebellar peduncle.
10. Nodulus.
11. Inferior medullary velum.
12. Horizontal fissure.
13. Flocculus.
14. Uvula of vermis.
15. Tonsil of cerebellum.
16. Biventral lobule.

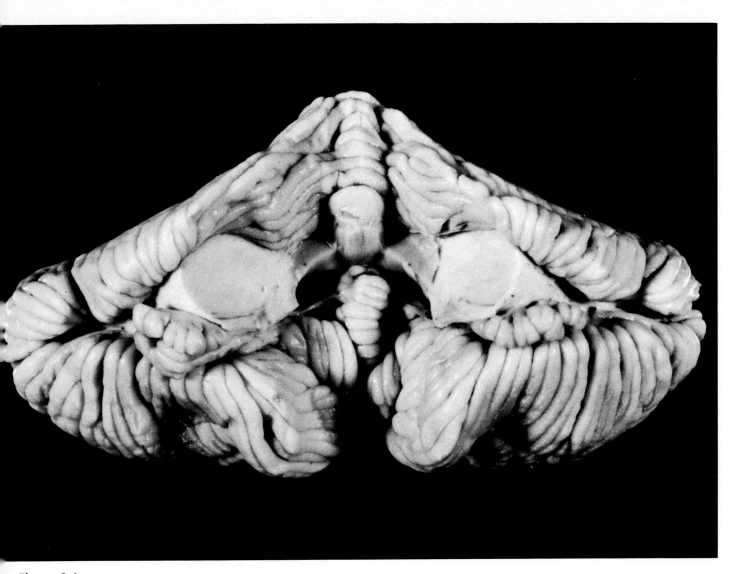

Figure 3-4.

3-5 Cerebellum sectioned sagittally to show the entire vermis

White matter that constitutes the core of the vermis is a narrow white zone from which primary white strips diverge; these in turn give rise to secondary white processes, more or less at right angles to the primary ones, which may give rise to other processes, all of which reach the cortical gray matter. The whole structure has the appearance of a tree with branches, and is known as the arbor vitae. The lingula of the vermis is slender, and applied closely to the superior medullary velum. The nodule of the vermis is more bulky, and attaches on each side to the inferior medullary velum. There is a deep, transverse fissure between the lingula and the nodule, producing a recess in the roof of the 4th ventricle. The wide and deep fissura prima is an easily recognizable landmark, separating the culmen from the declive.

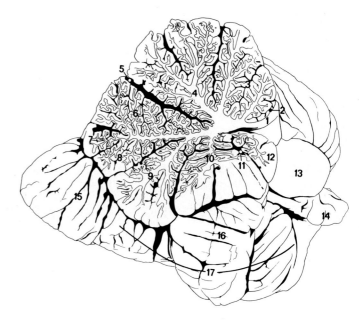

1. Superior medullary velum.
2. Lingula.
3. Central lobule.
4. Culmen.
5. Fissura prima.
6. Declive.
7. Folium vermis.
8. Tuber vermis.
9. Pyramis vermis.
10. Uvula.
11. Posterolateral fissure.
12. Nodulus.
13. Middle cerebellar peduncle.
14. Flocculus.
15. Inferior semilunar lobule.
16. Tonsil.
17. Biventral lobule.

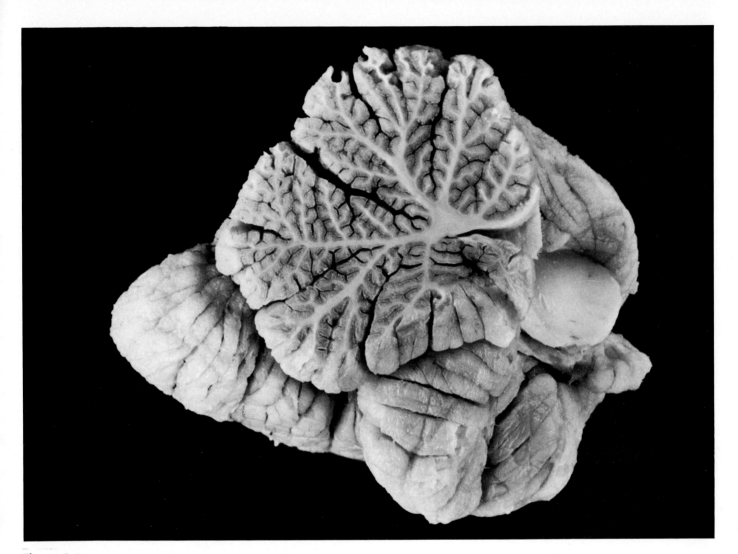

Figure 3-5.

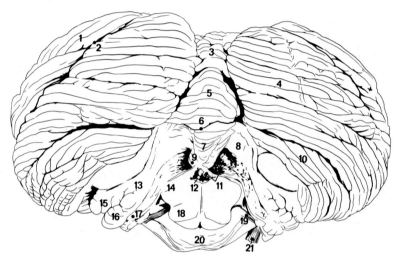

The tonsils and major parts of the biventer lobules have been removed. In the midline, the tuber, pyramid, uvula, and nodulus are seen on the inferior aspect of the vermis. In the lower part of the illustration is the cut surface of the medulla oblongata and a view of the ventral pons from below. Lateral to the nodulus is a thin, white lamina—the inferior medullary velum—which extends in a lateral direction into the peduncle of the flocculus.

The thin, dark, and highly vascular tela choroidea of the 4th ventricle is attached to the posterior margin of the inferior medullary velum and the peduncle of the flocculus. Two processes of the tela choroidea constitute the choroid plexuses of the 4th ventricle, and these can be seen near the midline through the transparent tela choroidea. The choroid plexuses are prolonged in a lateral direction across the inferior cerebellar peduncle, and they protrude through the lateral apertures of the 4th ventricle.

1. Superior semilunar lobule.
2. Horizontal fissure.
3. Tuber of vermis.
4. Inferior semilunar lobule.
5. Pyramid of vermis.
6. Fissura secunda.
7. Uvula of vermis.
8. Inferior medullary velum.
9. Nodulus of vermis.
10. Biventral lobule.
11. Tela choroidea of 4th ventricle.
12. 4th ventricle.
13. Peduncle of flocculus.
14. Inferior cerebellar peduncle.
15. Paraflocculus.
16. Flocculus.
17. Choroid plexus protruding through lateral aperture of 4th ventricle.
18. Olivary nucleus.
19. Facial nerve.
20. Pons.
21. Trigeminal nerve.

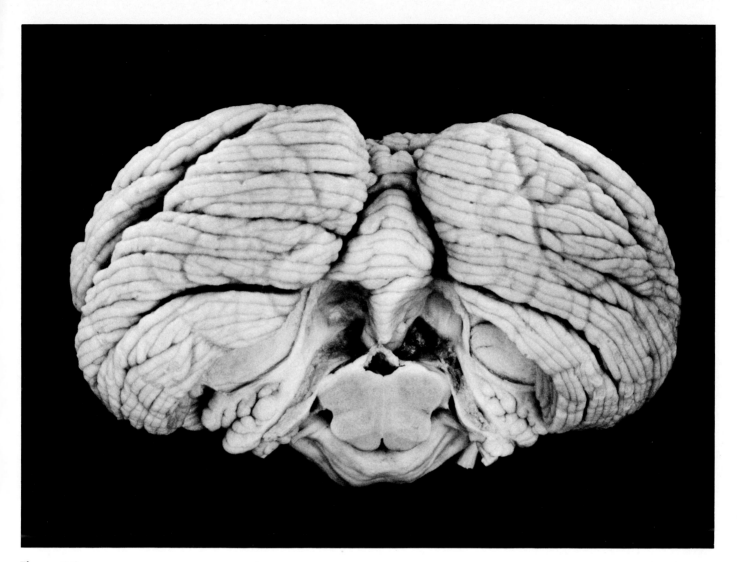

Figure 3-6.

The intracerebellar nuclei and outflow tracts have been isolated and are seen against a white background provided by the medullary substance of the cerebellum. The **dentate** nucleus is characterized by well-defined, almost parallel bars of gray matter, which are separated from each other by deep grooves, the contours having been filled with white, medullary substance. The main bulk of the superior cerebellar peduncle issues from the ventral aspect of the dentate nucleus.

The other smaller cerebellar nuclei are situated medial to the dentate. The **fastigial** nucleus is most medially placed, incorporated in the white substance of the anterior part of the superior vermis and forming a part of the roof of the 4th ventricle. On each side, ventrolateral to the fastigial nucleus, two small **globose** nuclei can be identified, while the **emboliform** nucleus occupies a more lateral position (and in this view is overlapped by the most medial column of the dentate nucleus). In this preparation the right emboliform nucleus is concealed by the medial margin of the right dentate nucleus. Delicate fiber tracts from these small cerebellar nuclei join together and subsequently merge with the main part of the superior cerebellar peduncle. The thin but distinct fiber bundle proceeding from the fastigial nucleus travels within the lateral margin of the superior medullary velum, presumably constituting the uncrossed component of the superior cerebellar peduncle, destined for the brain stem reticular formation. Note the fibers of the lateral and medial lemnisci arching around the dorsolateral side of the superior cerebellar peduncle to disappear into the midbrain tegmentum. Each trochlear nerve makes its exit through the tectum (that is, the dorsal portion) of the midbrain, immediately lateral to the frenulum of the superior medullary velum.

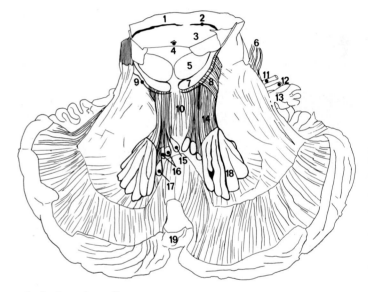

1. Basis pedunculi.
2. Substantia nigra.
3. Tegmentum of midbrain.
4. Cerebral aqueduct.
5. Superior colliculus.
6. Trigeminal nerve.
7. Inferior colliculus.
8. Lateral and medial lemnisci.
9. Trochlear nerve.
10. Superior medullary velum.
11. Facial nerve.
12. Vestibulocochlear nerve.
13. Flocculus.
14. Superior cerebellar peduncle.
15. Fastigial nucleus.
16. Globose nuclei.
17. Emboliform nucleus.
18. Dentate nucleus.
19. Vermis.

Figure 3-7.

The ventral parts of the vermis and cerebellar hemispheres have been dissected away. On each side, the **dentate** nucleus possesses numerous nodules of gray matter, arranged somewhat unevenly. These form the ventral terminations of gray columns which are seen in longitudinal array on the dorsal aspect of the dentate nucleus. A profusion of white fibers issuing from the ventral aspect of the dentate nucleus converge rostrally to form the main part of the superior cerebellar peduncle.

The other cerebellar nuclei are seen more medially. Near the midline, isolated in the white matter of the roof of the 4th ventricle, are the rather large, spherical **fastigial** nuclei. Two **globose** nuclei are present on each side; one is immediately lateral to the fastigial nucleus and the other is located more posteriorly against the elongated **emboliform** nucleus. A delicate fiber bundle emerges from each nucleus and joins the superior cerebellar peduncle. The bulky superior cerebellar peduncles cross each other to form the **decussation of the superior cerebellar peduncles,** located within the midbrain tegmentum.

1. Decussation of superior cerebellar peduncles.
2. Superior cerebellar peduncle.
3. Superior medullary velum.
4. Fastigial nucleus.
5. Globose nuclei.
6. Emboliform nucleus.
7. White matter of vermis.
8. Dentate nucleus.

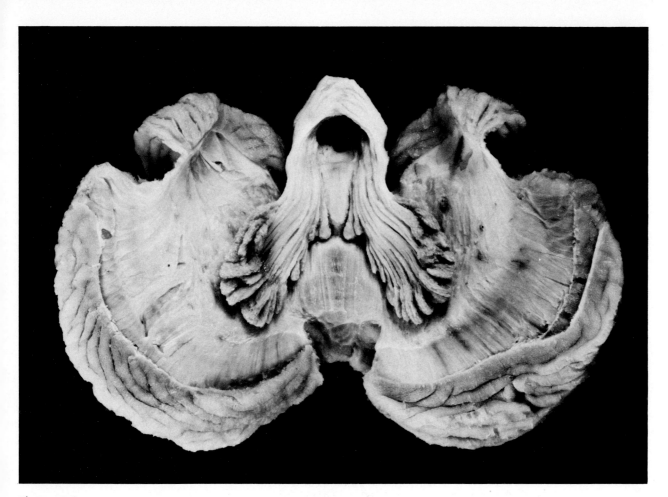

Figure 3-8.

3-9 Left side: horizontal section through the cerebellar hemisphere at the level of the dentate nucleus. Right side: dorsal view of intracerebellar nuclei and associated outflow tracts.

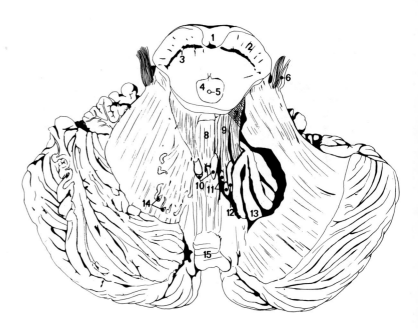

The cerebellar nuclei are presented in contrasting ways. On the **left** side, the gray laminae of the dentate nucleus surround the myelinated outflow tract which, issuing from the hilus, forms the bulk of the superior cerebellar peduncle.

The dissected **right** cerebellar hemisphere illustrates the deeply fluted columns of the dentate nucleus together with the smaller, more medially located globose, emboliform, and fastigial nuclei. These smaller nuclei are not easily observed in sections. Note that the main outflow pathways of all the intracerebellar nuclei tend to be in register, and that the dentate nucleus makes the largest contribution to the superior cerebellar peduncle.

1. Interpeduncular fossa.
2. Basis pedunculi.
3. Substantia nigra.
4. Central gray of midbrain.
5. Mesencephalic (cerebral) aqueduct.
6. Trigeminal nerve.
7. Lateral and medial lemnisci.
8. Superior medullary velum.
9. Superior cerebellar peduncle.
10. Fastigial nuclei.
11. Globose nuclei.
12. Emboliform nucleus.
13. Dentate nucleus.
14 Horizontal section through left dentate nucleus.
15. Vermis.

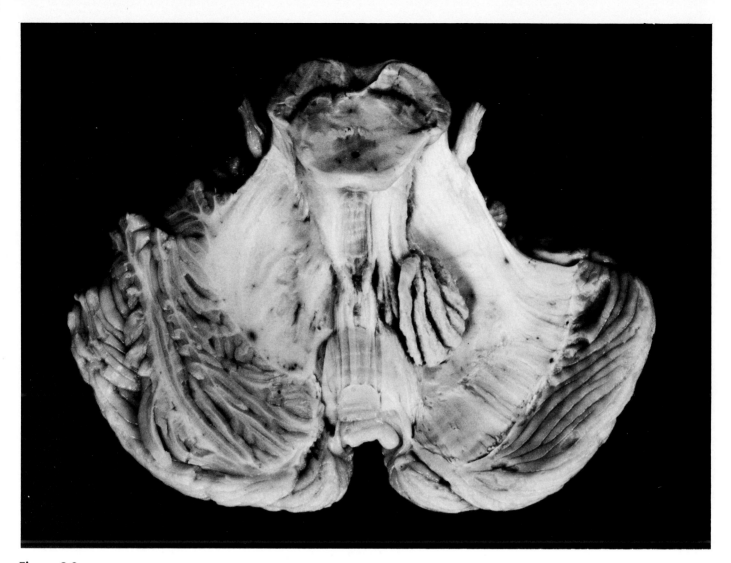

Figure 3-9.

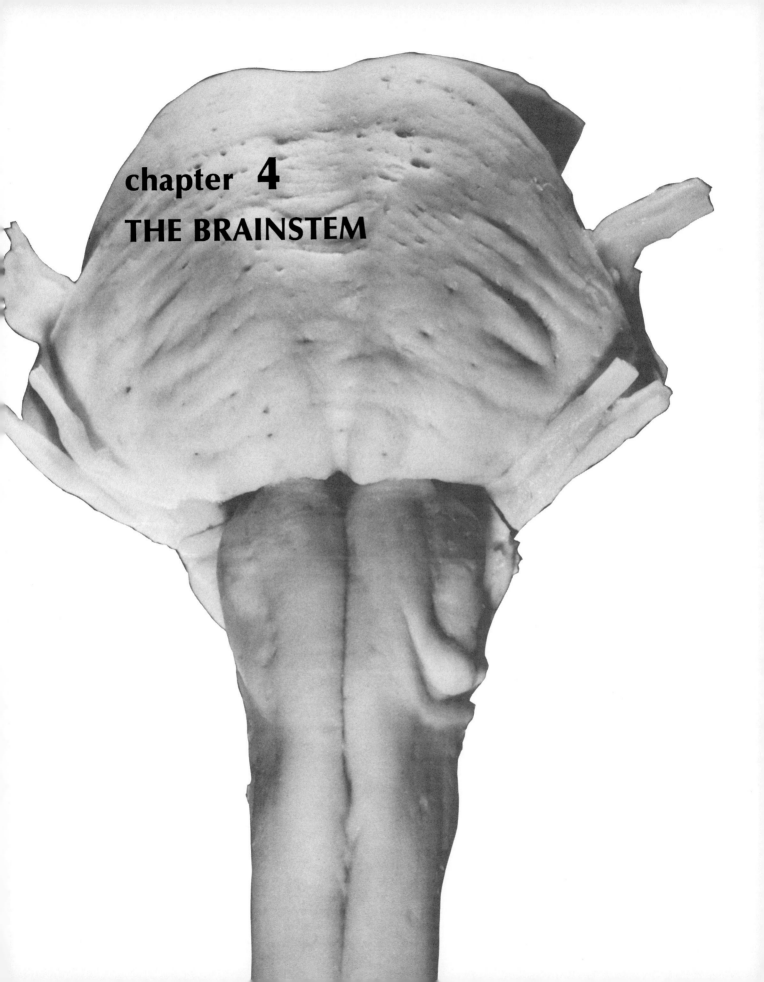

chapter **4**

THE BRAINSTEM

The middle cerebellar peduncle, which passes backwards and laterally from the pons into the cerebellar hemisphere, has been removed. The inferior cerebellar peduncle crosses the superior cerebellar peduncle. Most of the hemispheric terminations of the inferior cerebellar peduncle have been removed, but its branches of distribution to the cortex of the vermis remain. The dorsal surface of the dentate nucleus has been cleaned. Its efferents pass in a cranial direction into the midbrain through the superior cerebellar peduncle.

The descending fibers of the spinal tract of the trigeminal nerve can be observed ventromedial to the inferior cerebellar peduncle. The lateral and medial lemnisci are gathered together in a large bundle that passes around the dorsolateral surface of the superior cerebellar peduncle to reach the midbrain tegmentum. In the lower pontine region, fibers of the trapezoid body can be seen emerging from the lateral aspect of the medial lemniscus (which they have pierced); these turn upwards to form the lateral lemniscus, which ascends through the pons and midbrain to terminate in the lower auditory centers (inferior colliculus in the midbrain, and medial geniculate nucleus in the diencephalon). At the medullary level, the medial lemniscus (which contains the 2nd neuron axons on the pathway for proprioceptive and tactile sensibility) is found dorsal to the pyramidal tract and medial to the olivary nucleus. The disposition of the medial lemniscus alters in the upper part of the medulla so that, as it enters the pons, it is spread out in the coronal plane (that is, from side to side), as can be seen in the photograph of a transverse section through the pons.

The olivary nuclear complex has been dissected out from its capsule of myelinated fibers (sometimes referred to as the amiculum of the olive). Note the longitudinal grooves on the surface of the olivary nucleus. The lower part of the olive has been left undisturbed. The external arcuate fibers curving backwards across its surface converge to join the inferior cerebellar peduncle.

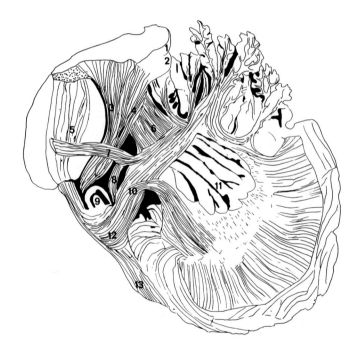

1. Superior colliculus.
2. Inferior colliculus.
3. Medial lemniscus.
4. Lateral lemniscus.
5. Sagittal section of pons.
6. Superior cerebellar peduncle.
7. Trigeminal nerve.
8. Spinal tract of trigeminal nerve.
9. Olivary nucleus.
10. Inferior cerebellar peduncle.
11. Dentate nucleus.
12. External arcuate fibers.
13. Medulla oblongata.

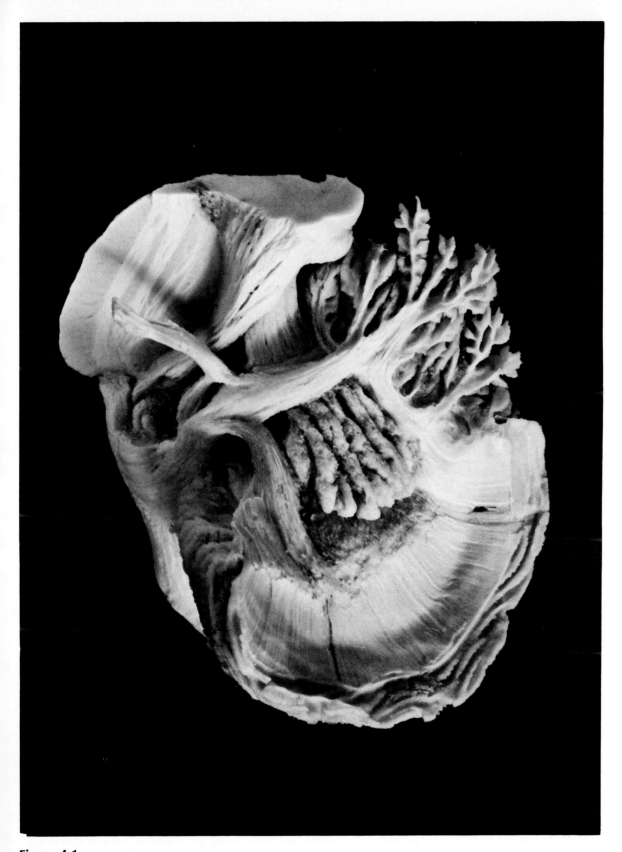

Figure 4-1.

4-2

Basal aspect of cerebellum and brain stem, showing cranial nerve attachments and some internal features of the medulla oblongata

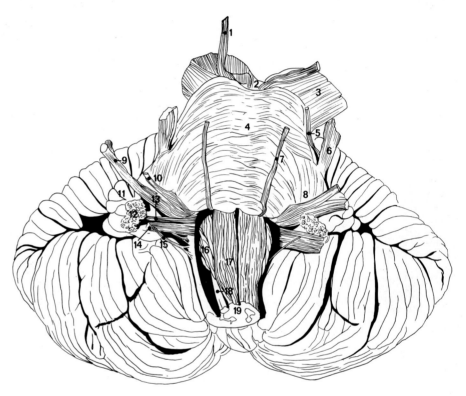

The pyramidal tracts in the ventral portion of the medulla oblongata have been exposed. Traced inferiorly, the tracts begin to reorganize in the pyramidal decussation (seen on the section through the medulla). At the level of decussation, the ventral (anterior) gray column of the spinal cord is separated from the central gray matter by the bundles of decussating fibers. The ventral gray matter of the cord continues uninterrupted into the hypoglossal nucleus. The surface of the olivary nucleus on the right side has been cleaned to display the characteristic longitudinally and obliquely placed gray ridges on its convex outer surface. The olivary nucleus extends upwards almost to the pontine level.

1. Oculomotor nerve.
2. Interpeduncular fossa.
3. Basis pedunculi.
4. Basilar sulcus of pons.
5. Motor (minor) root of trigeminal nerve.
6. Sensory (major) root of trigeminal nerve.
7. Abducent nerve.
8. Middle cerebellar peduncle.
9. Vestibulocochlear nerve.
10. Facial nerve.
11. Flocculus.
12. Choroid plexus protruding through lateral aperture of 4th ventricle.
13. Glossopharyngeal nerve.
14. Vagus nerve.
15. Accessory nerve.
16. Olivary nucleus.
17. Pyramidal tract.
18. Hypoglossal nucleus.
19. Pyramidal decussation.

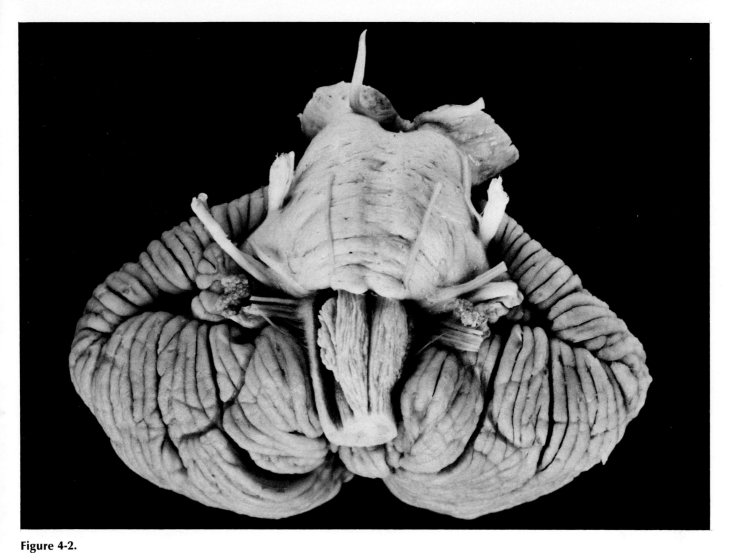

Figure 4-2.

Ventral surface of medulla oblongata and pons

Removal of the meninges and some cranial nerve roots allow salient features of the ventral or anterior aspect of these parts to be examined more easily. The deep anterior median fissure of the spinal cord is continued into the medulla oblongata, but is interrupted in the lower part of the medulla by descending corticospinal fibers which leave the pyramids in successive bundles to cross obliquely to the opposite sides, thereby forming the pyramidal decussation. These decussating bundles can be seen distinctly between the lips of the ventral median fissure. The pyramids rapidly diminish in size alongside the decussation, reflecting the fact that the great majority of corticospinal fibers leave the pyramids at the decussation. On the surface of the left pyramid (right side of the illustration), a ridge is created by a large group of fibers that leave the pyramid and arch around the lower end of the olive. This ridge is the surface landmark for the fasciculus circumolivaris pyramidis, which forms part of the so-called aberrant cortico-ponto-cerebellar pathway. The latter terminates on the nucleus of the fasciculus circumolivaris, which lies against the dorsolateral surface of the inferior cerebellar peduncle.

Note the great girth of the pons, caused by transverse pontine fibers which enter the thick, compact middle cerebellar peduncles. The shallow midline basilar sulcus is accounted for by the presence, on each side, of descending corticospinal fibers which tunnel through the ventral pons to reach the pyramids of the medulla.

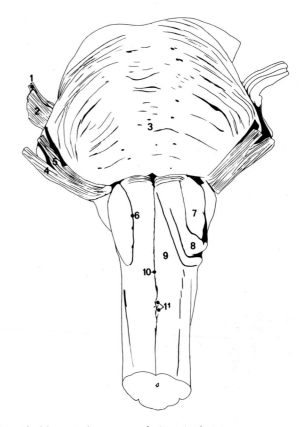

1. Motor (minor) root of trigeminal nerve.
2. Sensory (major) root of trigeminal nerve.
3. Basilar sulcus of pons.
4. Vestibulocochlear nerve.
5. Facial nerve.
6. Ventrolateral sulcus of medulla oblongata.
7. Olive.
8. Circumolivary bundle.
9. Pyramid of medulla oblongata.
10. Ventral (anterior) median fissure.
11. Pyramidal decussation.

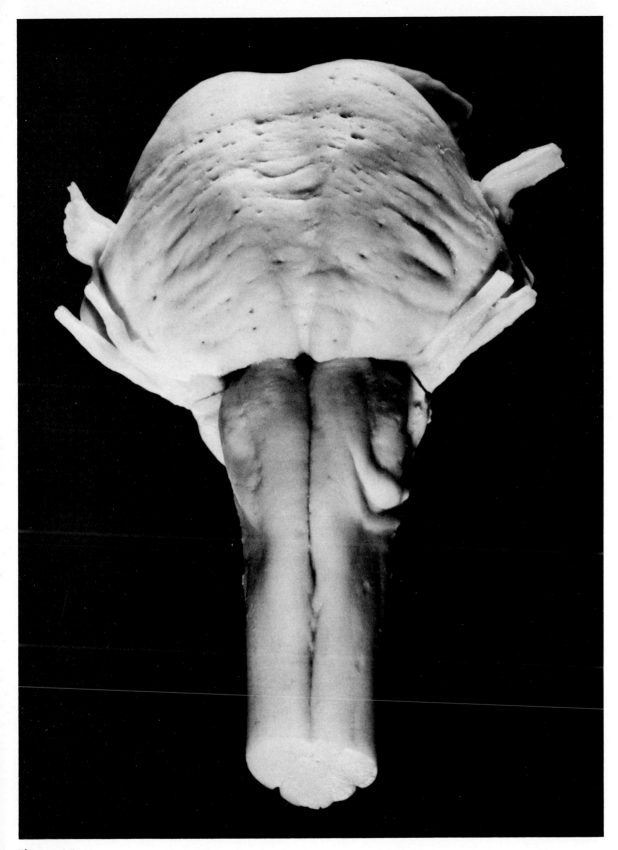

Figure 4-3.

4-4 Brainstem: dorsal view

Dorsal surfaces of the medulla oblongata, pons, midbrain, and part of the diencephalon are shown after removal of the cerebellum. Key features are the cut surfaces of the cerebellar peduncles and the diamond-shaped floor of the 4th ventricle (rhomboid fossa). The posterior part of the pineal body is seen above and between the two superior colliculi of the midbrain. Between the two inferior colliculi the frenulum of the superior medullary velum is attached to the lamina tecti. On each side of the frenulum, the trochlear nerve emerges. Medial and lateral geniculate bodies are located against the inferior aspect of the pulvinar of the thalamus.

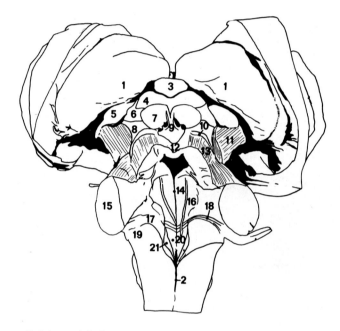

1. Pulvinar of thalamus.
2. Posterior median sulcus.
3. Pineal body.
4. Superior colliculus.
5. Medial geniculate body.
6. Brachium of inferior colliculus.
7. Inferior colliculus.
8. Lemniscal trigone.
9. Frenulum of superior medullary velum.
10. Trochlear nerve.
11. Basis pedunculi.
12. Superior medullary velum.
13. Superior cerebellar peduncle.
14. Median sulcus of rhomboid fossa.
15. Middle cerebellar peduncle.
16. Facial colliculus.
17. Vestibular area.
18. Striae medullares of 4th ventricle.
19. Inferior cerebellar peduncle.
20. Hypoglossal trigone.
21. Vagal trigone.

Figure 4-4.

The insula is a portion of the cerebral cortex that is not visible until the margins of the lateral sulcus are opened up, or, as in this case, removed. The insular cortex is roughly triangular. (Branches of the middle cerebral artery and the deep cerebral veins have been removed to display the sulci and gyri.) Originally part of the superficial cortex, it later became submerged beneath the expanding cortex around it, thereby remaining relatively close to the basal ganglia of the hemisphere. Complete submergence of the insular cortex is a human characteristic, not attained even by the apes. Between the superior cerebellar peduncle and the basis pedunculi, the fibers of the lateral lemniscus ascend at the surface of the midbrain tegmentum. The majority of nerve fibers in the superior cerebellar peduncle arise from cell bodies in the intracerebellar nuclei. The middle cerebellar peduncle is much the largest of the three, and is placed lateral to the other peduncles. It is composed of the transverse pontine fibers, which are the axons of neurons in the pontine nuclei. These are the second neurons of the extensive cortico-ponto-cerebellar pathway. The inferior cerebellar peduncle connects the medulla to the cerebellum, which it enters between the middle peduncle (laterally) and the superior peduncle (medially). The superior cerebellar peduncles plunge into the tegmentum of the midbrain. Prominent in a lateral view of the medulla is the oval, circumscribed elevation known as the olive. The fibers of the circumolivary fascicle arch around its lower end.

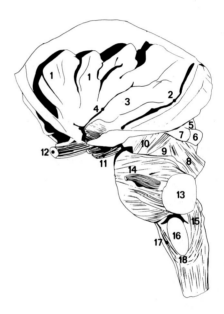

1. Short gyri of insula.
2. Circular sulcus of insula.
3. Long gyrus of insula.
4. Central sulcus of insula.
5. Superior colliculus.
6. Inferior colliculus.
7. Brachium of inferior colliculus.
8. Superior cerebellar peduncle.
9. Lemniscal trigone.
10. Basis pedunculi.
11. Oculomotor nerve.
12. Optic nerve.
13. Middle cerebellar peduncle.
14. Trigeminal nerve.
15. Inferior cerebellar peduncle.
16. Olive.
17. Pyramid of medulla oblongata.
18. Circumolivary bundle.

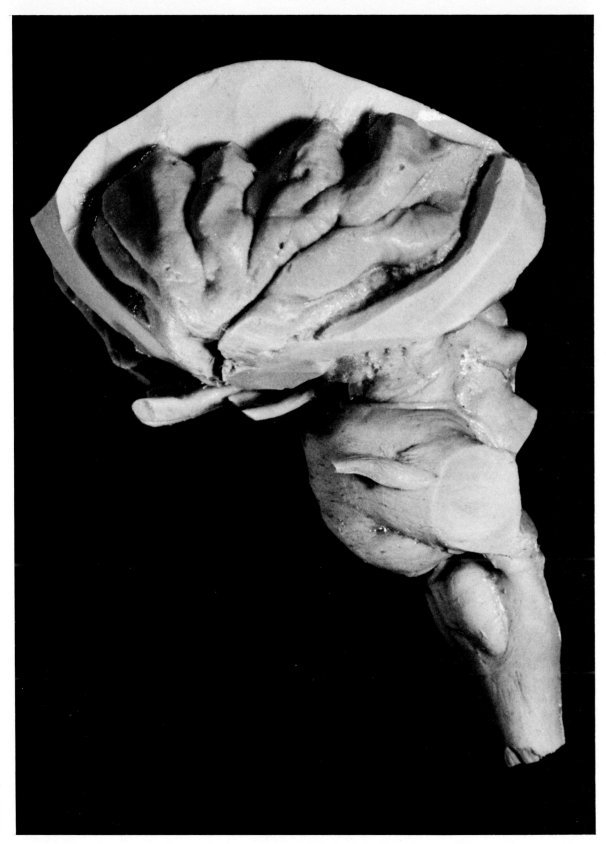

Figure 4-5.

The primary fissure cuts deep into the dorsal surface of the cerebellum between the culmen and declive, together with their extensions into each hemisphere. The folium and the tuber of the vermis, together with the superior and inferior semilunar lobules of the hemispheres, are readily seen. Immediately in front of the pineal body is the thin white habenular commissure. On each side, the habenular nucleus causes a protrusion at the surface of the habenular trigone. Anteriorly the habenular trigone is prolonged into a white band—the stria medullaris thalami—which separates the dorsal and medial surfaces of the thalamus. Removal of the crura and the body of the fornix has left the medial part of the dorsal surface of the thalamus rather rough, whereas the lateral part is covered by the smooth lamina affixa. The sharp medial margin of the lamina affixa—the tenia choroidea—marks the line of attachment of the tela choroidea of the lateral ventricle. More anteriorly, note the lamina of the septum pellucidum on each side of the cavum of the septum pellucidum.

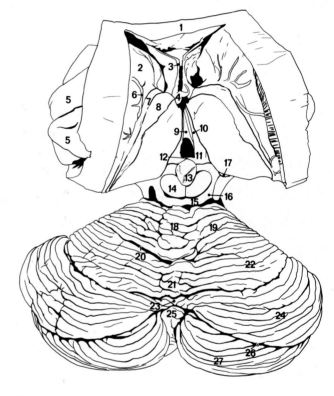

1. Genu of corpus callosum.
2. Head of caudate nucleus.
3. Lamina of septum pellucidum.
4. Columns of fornix.
5. Short gyri of insula.
6. Tributary of thalamostriate vein.
7. Stria terminalis.
8. Lamina affixa.
9. Interthalamic adhesion.
10. Stria medullaris thalami.
11. Habenular trigone.
12. Habenular commissure.
13. Pineal body.
14. Superior (cranial) colliculus.
15. Inferior colliculus.
16. Brachium of inferior (caudal) colliculus.
17. Medial geniculate body.
18. Culmen.
19. Quadrangular lobule.
20. Fissura prima.
21. Declive.
22. Lobulus simplex.
23. Folium of vermis.
24. Superior semilunar lobule.
25. Tuber of vermis.
26. Horizontal fissure.
27. Inferior semilunar lobule.

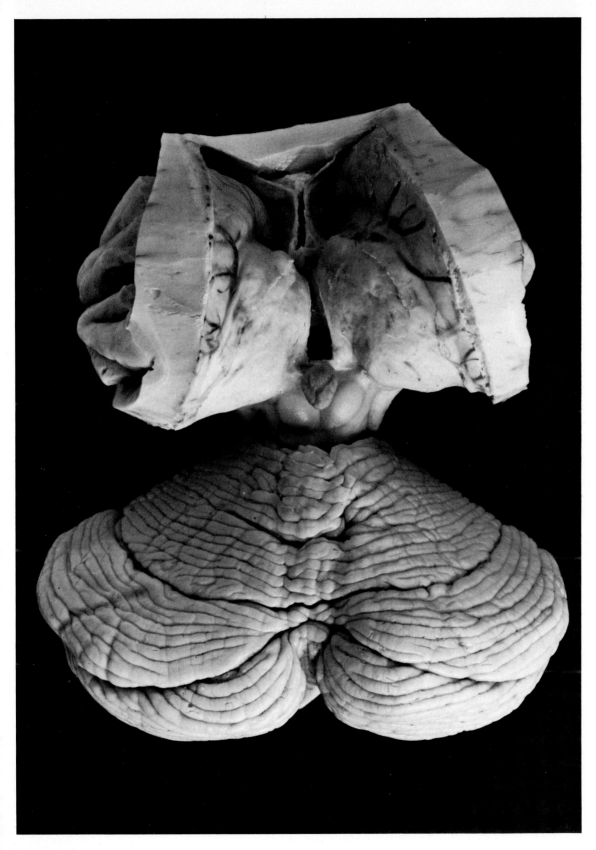

Figure 4-6.

4-7 Transverse section through lower medulla oblongata showing pyramidal (motor) decussation (Weigert stained)

At the level of the foramen magnum, where the spinal cord ends and the medulla oblongata begins, the gray matter undergoes a marked reorganization. In the decussation of the pyramids, the bundles of corticospinal fibers detach the ventral gray matter from the central gray substance. The central canal and surrounding gray matter appear as though pushed dorsally by the decussating bundles of axons. At least three-quarters of the pyramidal fibers which arise in the cerebral cortex and descend through the pyramids of the medulla cross at the decussation, most of the remainder forming the uncrossed ventral corticospinal tract. The latter peters out in the thoracic spinal cord as its axons gradually cross to reach the ventral gray horn of the opposite side.

Adjacent to the dorsal median septum is the nucleus gracilis, skirted by the fasciculus gracilis, which comes to an end as its primary sensory axons terminate in the nucleus of the same name. Projecting posteriorly from the dorsal horn is the most caudal part of the nucleus cuneatus, which becomes more prominent at higher levels. The fasciculus cuneatus covers its nucleus and occupies the area immediately lateral to the fasciculus gracilis. The spinal (inferior) nucleus of the trigeminal nerve, which extends throughout the whole length of the medulla oblongata and continues into the spinal cord, is a much expanded counterpart of the substantia gelatinosa found in the dorsal gray horn of the spinal cord. The spinal tract of the trigeminal is a narrow band of fibers interposed between the spinal nucleus of the trigeminal and the periphery of the medulla oblongata.

1. Gracile fascicle.
2. Cuneate fascicle.
3. Gracile nucleus.
4. Cuneate nucleus.
5. Spinal nucleus of trigeminal nerve.
6. Spinal tract of trigeminal nerve.
7. Central canal.
8. Dorsal spinocerebellar tract.
9. Ventral spinocerebellar tract.
10. Pyramidal (motor) decussation.
11. Pyramidal tract.

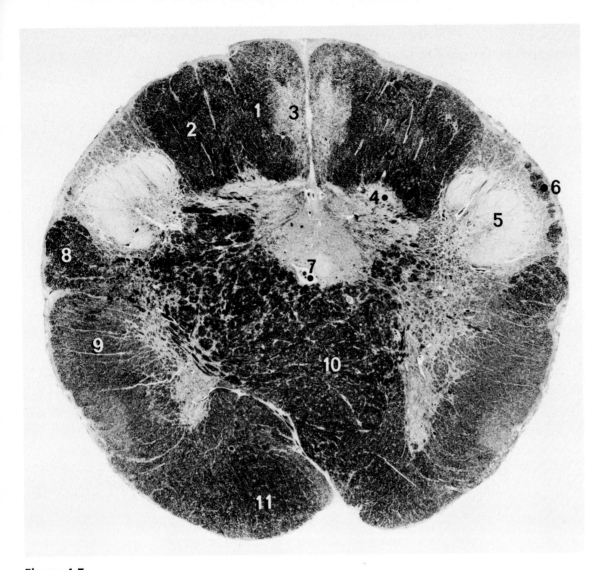

Figure 4-7.

4-8 Medulla oblongata, cut transversely through the decussation of the medial lemnisci (Weigert stained)

The nucleus gracilis is located in the medial part of the posterior funiculus, surrounded by a thin rim of fibers belonging to the fasciculus gracilis, which terminate in the nucleus. The nucleus cuneatus has a wider fringe of fibers, which belong to the fasciculus cuneatus.

The sensory decussation is the key feature of this section. Numerous internal arcuate fibers arise from gracile and cuneate nuclei, take a semicircular course through the reticular formation and around the central gray substance, and decussate with the corresponding fibers of the opposite side to form the sensory decussation. The curving internal arcuate fibers pass between the spinal (inferior) nucleus of the trigeminal nerve and the central gray, After decussating, these fibers ascend in a compact, ribbon-like tract called the medial lemniscus. Dorsolateral to the pyramidal tract, the medial accessory olivary nucleus, which is not present at lower levels, has just appeared. In the ventral part of the central gray is the hypoglossal nucleus, the main source of motor fibers to the tongue. Some fibers of the hypoglossal nerve can be traced through the reticular formation towards the ventrolateral sulcus.

1. Median dorsal sulcus.
2. Gracile fascicle.
3. Gracile nucleus.
4. Cuneate fascicle.
5. Cuneate nucleus.
6. Spinal tract of trigeminal nerve.
7. Dorsal spinocerebellar tract.
8. Spinal (inferior) nucleus of trigeminal nerve.
9. Hypoglossal nucleus.
10. Ventral spinocerebellar tract.
11. Internal arcuate fibers.
12. Decussation of medial lemnisci.
13. Medial accessory olivary nucleus.
14. Fibers of hypoglossal nerve.
15. Pyramidal tract.
16. Ventral median fissure.

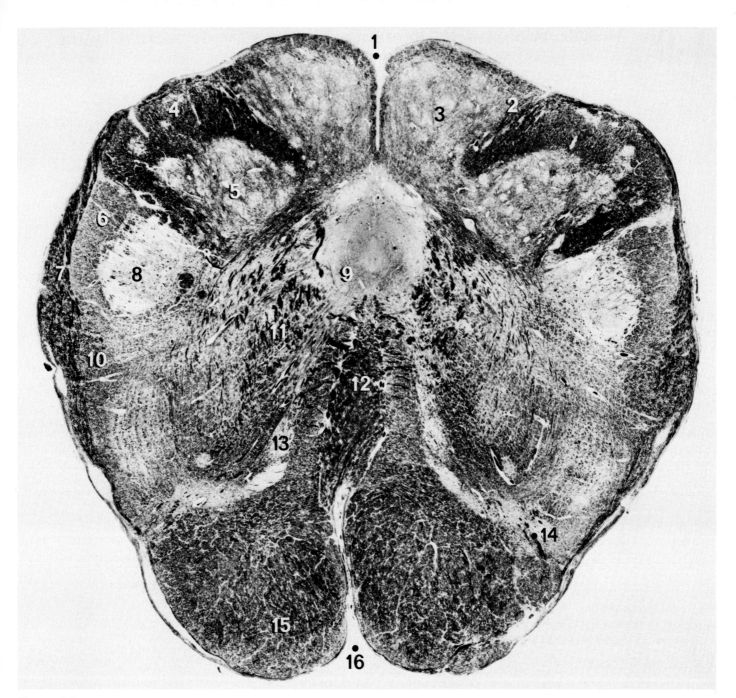

Figure 4-8.

4-9 Midsection of medulla oblongata (Weigert stained)

The caudal or main olivary nucleus is conspicuous, and the dorsal and medial accessory nuclei are seen also. The main nucleus is a crenated, thin gray lamina with a well-defined hilus through which a multitude of olivocerebellar tract fibers issue, traversing both medial lemnisci and the olivary nucleus of the opposite side to reach the contralateral inferior cerebellar peduncle.

Several nuclei can be recognized in the floor of the 4th ventricle. Most medial is the circular profile of the hypoglossal nucleus, representing the somatic motor column of brainstem nuclei. Fibers of the hypoglossal nerve take a ventrolateral course and emerge between the olive and pyramid. More laterally placed are the dorsal motor nucleus of the vagus (a general visceral motor nucleus) and the medial and caudal vestibular nuclei (special somatic afferent nuclei). Ventrolateral to the dorsal motor nucleus of the vagus are the nucleus and tractus solitarius, concerned with visceral pain (general visceral afferent component) and taste (special visceral afferent component). It is thought that axons from nerve cells of the solitary nucleus project to the thalamus, with subsequent relay of information to the cerebral cortex. The spinal nucleus of the trigeminal nerve, with its tract placed lateral to it, is classified as a general somatic afferent nucleus.

The medial longitudinal fasciculus and the tectospinal tract are located close to the median raphe, ventromedial to the hypoglossal nucleus. Dorsal to the olivary nuclei is the extensive reticular formation of the medulla, composed of diffusely disposed neurons interspersed by ascending and descending myelinated axons belonging to a variety of pathways.

1. Hypoglossal nucleus.
2. Dorsal vagal nucleus.
3. Medial vestibular nucleus.
4. Inferior (caudal) vestibular nucleus and vestibulospinal tract.
5. Nucleus of solitary tract.
6. Solitary tract.
7. Spinal nucleus of trigeminal nerve.
8. Spinal tract of trigeminal nerve.
9. Inferior cerebellar peduncle.
10. Medial longitudinal fascicle with tectospinal tract.
11. Dorsal accessory olivary nucleus.
12. Fibers of olivocerebellar tract.
13. Caudal olivary nucleus.
14. Hilus of caudal olivary nucleus.
15. Medial lemniscus and olivocerebellar fibers.
16. Medial accessory olivary nucleus.
17. Pyramidal tract.

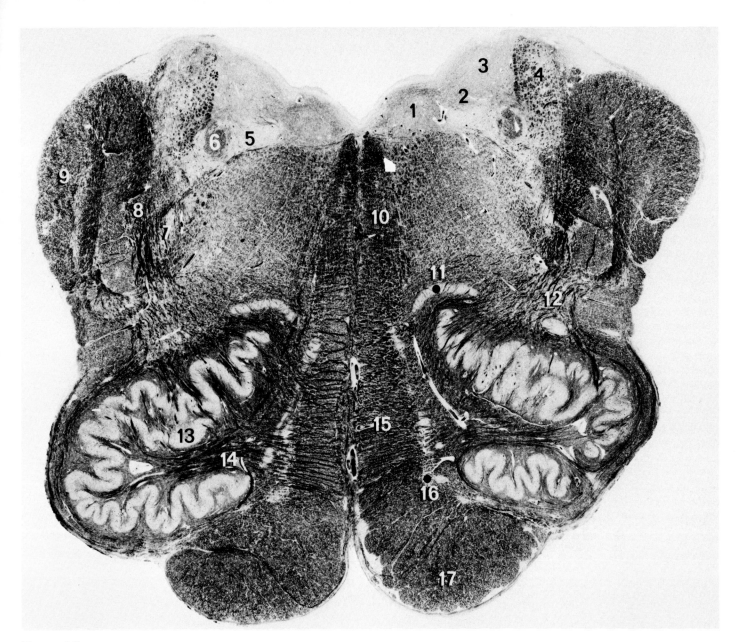

Figure 4-9.

4-10 Transverse section through lower pons, passing through the facial colliculi (Weigert stained)

The facial colliculi are marked prominences in the floor of the 4th ventricle. Each facial colliculus is produced by the underlying nucleus of the abducent nerve together with the genu of the facial nerve curving around the nucleus. The facial nucleus itself is placed more ventrally, and the unusual course of its axons—prior to their emergence from the brain at the cerebellopontine angle—is worthy of attention.

The medial longitudinal fasciculus occupies its characteristic paramedian position. The ascending fibers of the medial lemniscus are intersected by transversely running fibers of the trapezoid body, which then turn upwards and become aggregated to form the lateral lemniscus. The trigeminal and spinal lemnisci also are located in the ventral part of the pontine tegmentum.

Lateral to the abducens nucleus is the lateral vestibular nucleus, which gives rise to the vestibulospinal tract; ventrolateral to the abducens nucleus are the spinal nucleus and tract of the trigeminal nerve. In the ventral portion of the pons are the scattered nests of cells that constitute the pontine nuclei, together with transverse pontine fibers which come together dorsolaterally in the massive middle cerebellar peduncles. Corticospinal and corticonuclear fibers descend in large bundles at this level, destined for the pyramids of the medulla oblongata.

1. Vermis of cerebellum.
2. Dentate nucleus.
3. 4th ventricle.
4. Abducens nucleus.
5. Genu of facial nerve.
6. Facial colliculus.
7. Lateral vestibular nucleus.
8. Spinal nucleus of trigeminal nerve.
9. Spinal tract of trigeminal nerve.
10. Facial nucleus.
11. Medial longitudinal fascicle.
12. Reticular formation.
13. Fibers of facial nerve.
14. Central tegmental tract.
15. Medial lemniscus and trapezoid body.
16. Spinal and trigeminal lemnisci.
17. Middle cerebellar peduncle.
18. Pontine nuclei and transverse pontine fibers.
19. Pyramidal tract.

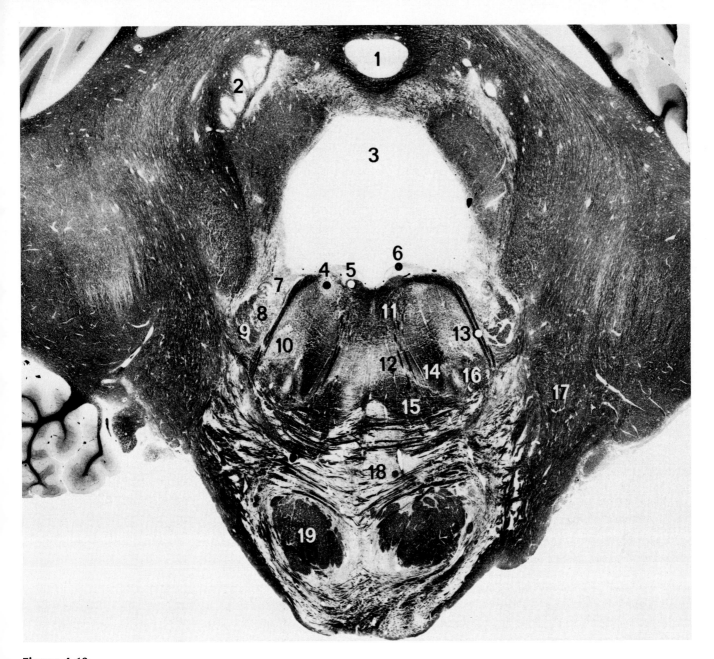

Figure 4-10.

Two areas of the pons can be differentiated: ventral and dorsal. In the ventral part, bundles of motor fibers—corticopontine, corticonuclear, and corticospinal—continue their descent from the basis pedunculi. These longitudinal bundles are separated from each other by the transverse pontine fibers and the widely scattered pontine nuclei that give rise to them. The transverse pontine fibers are continued into the middle cerebellar peduncles, the projections from pontine nuclei to cerebellar cortex being known as the pontocerebellar fibers. The mingling of gray and white matter in the ventral part of the pons produces a striped appearance which is similar at all pontine levels.

The dorsal or tegmental part of the pons varies in its internal structure at different levels. The level illustrated contains both sensory and motor trigeminal nuclei. The principal (pontine) sensory nucleus of the trigeminal nerve lies ventral to the superior cerebellar peduncle and medial to the middle cerebellar peduncle. The motor nucleus is ventromedial to the principal (pontine) sensory nucleus, and both nuclei are in line with the oblique axis of the trigeminal nerve which pierces the ventrolateral part of the pons. In this section the medial lemniscus is located near the ventral limit of the dorsal part of the pons, separated by a short interval from the median raphe. Note the locations of the trigeminal, spinal, and lateral lemnisci. The medial longitudinal fasciculus retains its paramedian position, and the central tegmental tract is surrounded by the loose substance of the reticular formation, situated dorsal to the medial lemniscus.

1. Cortex of cerebellar hemisphere.
2. Lingula.
3. Superior cerebellar peduncle.
4. Superior medullary velum.
5. 4th ventricle.
6. Medial longitudinal fascicle.
7. Principal (pontine) sensory nucleus of trigeminal nerve.
8. Motor nucleus of trigeminal nerve.
9. Central tegmental tract.
10. Medial lemniscus.
11. Trigeminal and spinal lemnisci.
12. Fibers of trigeminal nerve.
13. Middle cerebellar peduncle.
14. Pontine nuclei and transverse pontine fibers.
15. Corticospinal and corticonuclear fibers.

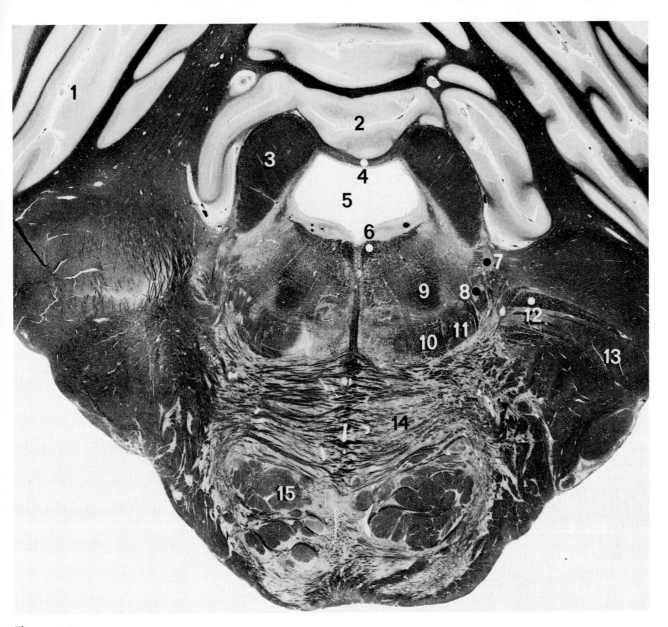

Figure 4-11.

4-12 Transverse section through the upper part of the pons (Weigert stained)

The 4th ventricle is diminished compared to its size in lower pons sections. This ventricle is continued cranially into the cerebral aqueduct of the midbrain. The superior medullary velum constitutes the thin roof of the ventricle, which stretches between two superior cerebellar peduncles. In the lateral margin of the central gray matter is the slender mesencephalic tract of the trigeminal nerve, with the mesencephalic nucleus placed on its medial side. The medial longitudinal fasciculus is found in its characteristic paramedian position. The central tegmental tract is a large bundle cut transversely as it passes through the pontine reticular formation.

In the lateral part of the tegmentum of the pons are four lemnisci (ribbons of white matter). At this level the medial lemniscus is oriented transversely and lies against the ventral part of the pons. Dorsal to the medial lemniscus is the trigeminal lemniscus, and dorsolateral to it is the spinal lemniscus. The lateral lemniscus is a vertically oriented strip of white matter ascending close to the lateral margin of the dorsal part of the pons. These four pairs of lemnisci proceed upwards into the tegmentum of the midbrain.

The ventral part of the pons contains chiefly white matter, composed of transverse pontine fibers intersecting longitudinal bundles of corticospinal, conticopontine and corticonuclear fibers. The transverse pontine fibers connect nests of pontine nuclei with the cerebellar cortex of the opposite side, via the middle cerebellar peduncles.

1. Superior medullary velum.
2. Mesencephalic tract of trigeminal nerve.
3. 4th ventricle.
4. Medial longitudinal fascicle.
5. Superior cerebellar peduncle.
6. Lateral lemniscus.
7. Spinal and trigeminal lemnisci.
8. Medial lemniscus.
9. Central tegmental tract.
10. Pontine nuclei and transverse pontine fibers.
11. Corticospinal and corticonuclear fibers.

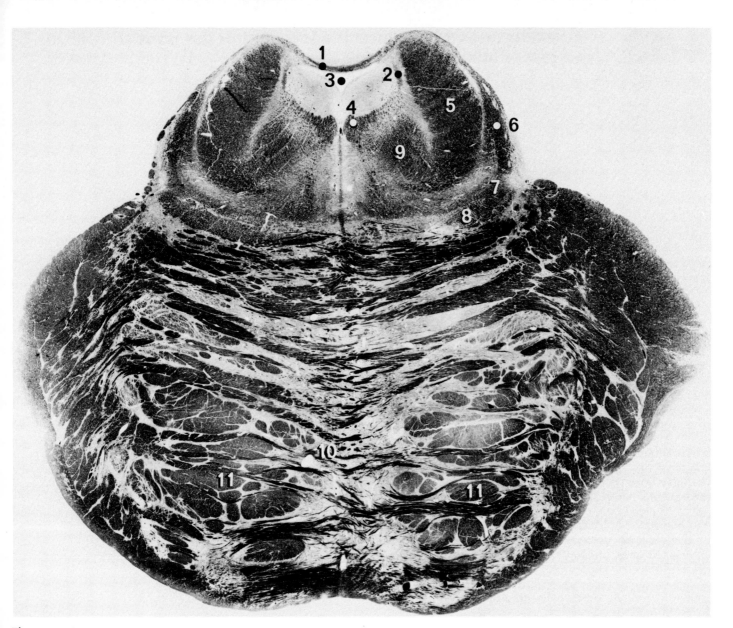

Figure 4-12.

4-13 Section through midbrain at the level of inferior (caudal) colliculi and tegmentum, and through the ventral pons (Weigert stained)

When sections are made through the brainstem, elements of the ventral part of the pons (which in man is very extensive) are commonly included with lower midbrain sections. At this level the most valuable aid to identification is the decussation of the superior cerebellar peduncles, which occupies a large part of the tegmentum. Situated more posteriorly is the aqueduct and, in the ventral margin of the gray matter surrounding the aqueduct, the trochlear nucleus. Just ventral to this nucleus is the medial longitudinal fasciculus which extends throughout the brainstem in this characteristic paramedian position. More laterally is a wide area occupied by the reticular formation of the midbrain tegmentum. This area is pierced by the longitudinally directed central tegmental tract. The peripheral part of the tegmentum accommodates four pairs of lemnisci. The medial lemniscus is detectable in this preparation as a narrow, dark strip; the trigeminal lemniscus (trigemino-thalamic fibers) and spinal lemniscus (spino-thalamic fibers) being located dorsolateral to it. The medial and spinal lemnisci are great pathways by which sensations are transmitted from one half of the body to the thalamus of the opposite side: the trigeminal lemnisci convey ordinary sensations from the head region to the thalami. The lateral lemniscus carries auditory signals, and is a narrow ribbon of fibers connected dorsally to the gray matter of the inferior colliculus (which is one of the centers for processing these auditory signals). The brachium of the inferior colliculus emerges from the latter and passes to the medial geniculate body. The ventral part of the section shows features characteristic of the ventral part of the pons, which is described in the pages devoted to the pons.

1. Nucleus of inferior (caudal) colliculus.
2. Brachium of inferior colliculus.
3. Mesencephalic (cerebral) aqueduct.
4. Lateral lemniscus.
5. Medial longitudinal fascicle.
6. Trochlear nucleus.
7. Central tegmental tract.
8. Spinal and trigeminal lemnisci.
9. Reticular formation of tegmentum.
10. Decussation of superior cerebellar peduncles.
11. Medial lemniscus.
12. Pontine nuclei and transverse pontine fibers.
13. Corticospinal and corticonuclear fibers.

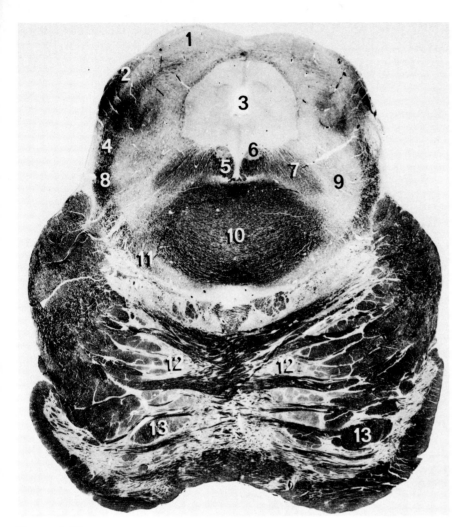

Figure 4-13.

The superior colliculi are a pair of ovoid masses composed of alternating layers of gray and white matter. They are centers for light reflexes and they interconnect with the spinal cord through the tectospinal and spinotectal tracts. The large nucleus of the medial geniculate body is lodged between the superior colliculus and the basis pedunculi, and receives the fibers of the brachium of the inferior colliculus. The motor nucleus of the oculomotor nerve is located in the ventral part of the central gray substance, and the fibers of the medial longitudinal fasciculus form a fringe on its ventrolateral side. The red nucleus is a landmark that distinguishes this brainstem level. In its medial part the red nucleus is pierced by axons that originate in the oculomotor nerve nuclei. Some dark streaks are caused by oculomotor nerve fibers that pass through the medial part of the substantia nigra to enter the interpeduncular fossa. Note the positions of the three lemnisci in the lateral part of the midbrain tegmentum, the medial lemniscus being ventrally placed. The basis pedunculi contains corticospinal and corticonuclear fibers which occupy the middle two-thirds of the basis, the corticopontine fibers occupying the medial and lateral edges of the basis pedunculi.

1. Superior (cranial) colliculus.
2. Brachium of inferior (caudal) colliculus.
3. Medial geniculate nucleus.
4. Spinal and trigeminal lemnisci.
5. Central gray substance.
6. Cerebral aqueduct.
7. Accessory nucleus of oculomotor nerve (Edinger-Westphal nucleus).
8. Oculomotor nucleus.
9. Medial lemniscus.
10. Central tegmental tract.
11. Medial longitudinal fascicle.
12. Red nucleus.
13. Fibers of oculomotor nerve.
14. Substantia nigra.
15. Basis pedunculi.

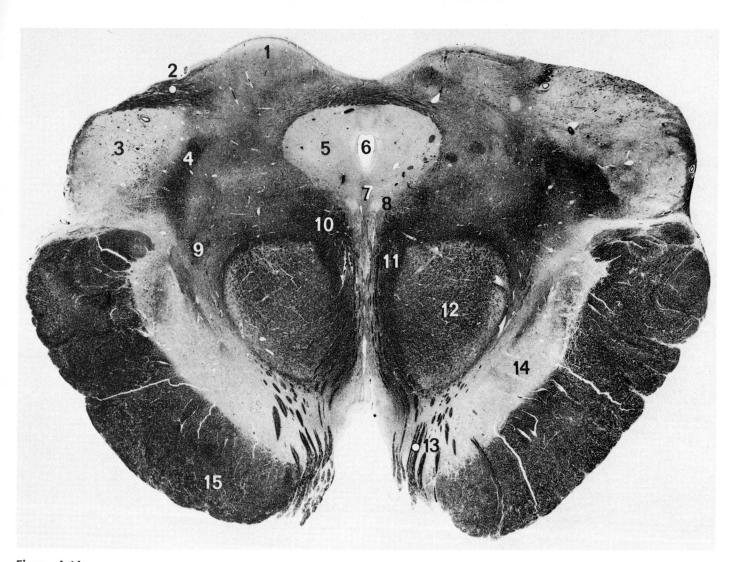

Figure 4-14.

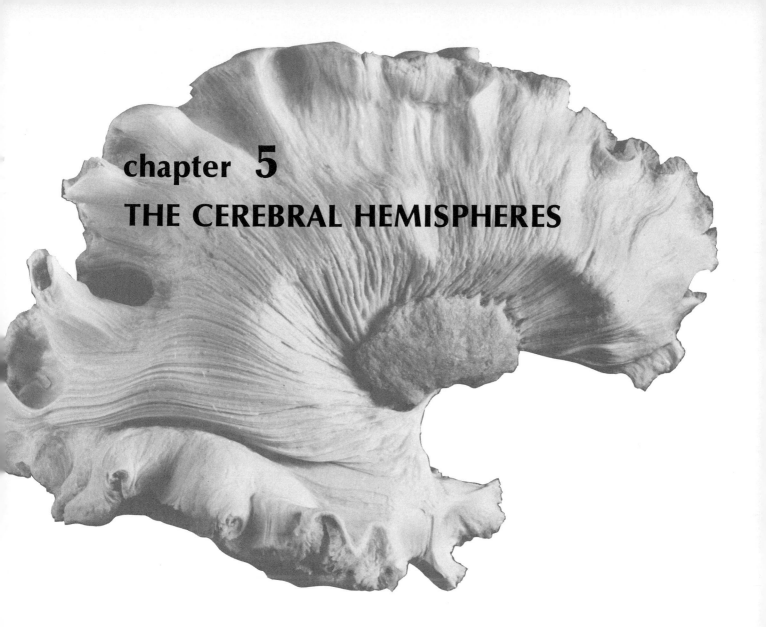

chapter **5**
THE CEREBRAL HEMISPHERES

Cerebral hemispheres from above (meninges and blood vessels removed). In this view, cerebrum conceals other parts of the brain.

The brain is ovoid, broader behind than in front. The longitudinal fissure is a narrow cleft that normally contains the falx cerebri (dura), arachnoid, pia, and cerebral arteries and veins, in particular the anterior cerebral vessels. The superolateral surface of each cerebral hemisphere is markedly convex and fits into the corresponding half of the skull vault. In this specimen, some atrophy of the cortex has resulted in separation of the gyri, so that the convolutions of the cerebral cortex can be readily appreciated. There is considerable individual variation in the patterns of gyri, and even the two sides of a brain differ in the arrangement of their convolutions. Interlocking gyri belonging to the right superior frontal gyrus can be seen on the right side of the brain. In the central sulcus of the left hemisphere, a short transverse gyrus is noteworthy.

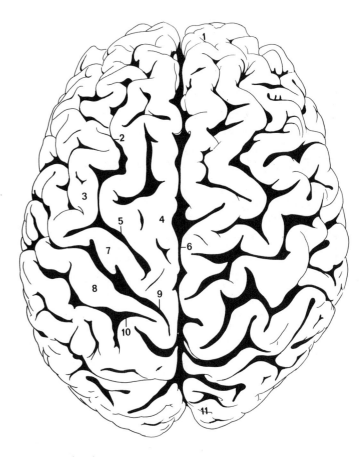

1. Frontal pole.
2. Superior frontal sulcus.
3. Middle frontal gyrus.
4. Superior frontal gyrus.
5. Precentral sulcus.
6. Longitudinal cerebral fissure.
7. Precentral gyrus.
8. Postcentral gyrus.
9. Central sulcus.
10. Postcentral sulcus.
11. Occipital pole.

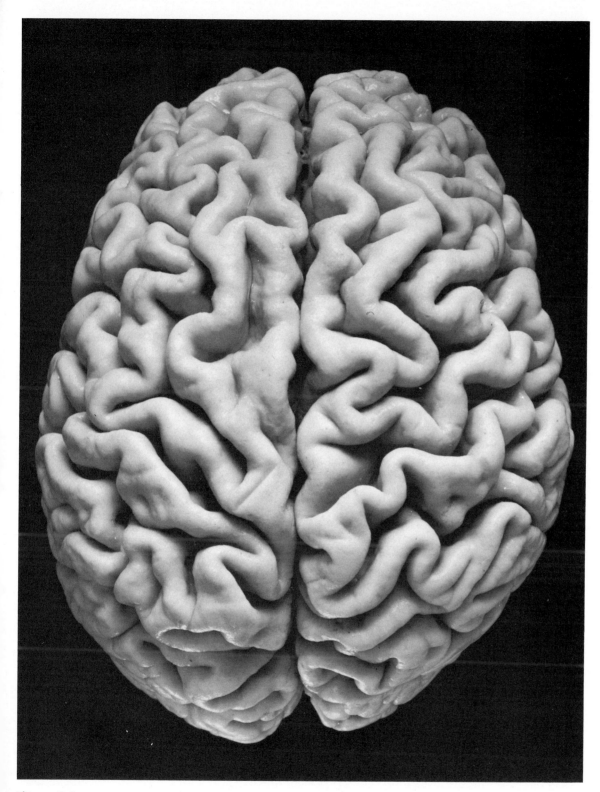

Figure 5-1.

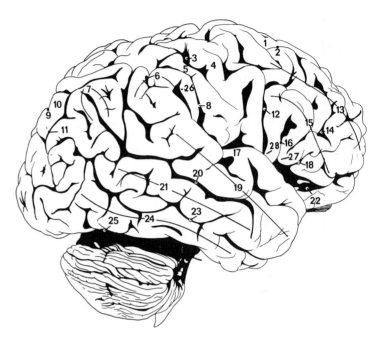

The stem of the lateral sulcus is a deep transverse furrow, from which the middle cerebral vessels have been removed. Above the temporal pole of the hemisphere, the posterior ramus of the lateral sulcus is a long cleft that runs backwards with an upwards inclination, and it enters the inferior parietal lobule where it may terminate in a T-shaped manner. The horizontal anterior and ascending rami of the lateral sulcus are well developed, although in other specimens it is sometimes difficult to identify them. On the left side of the brain (in most right-handed individuals), the opercular and triangular parts of the inferior frontal gyrus are referred to as Broca's area, which is associated with the processing and transmission of motor elements of speech. The lower part of the precentral gyrus is very wide and incompletely subdivided by longitudinal sulci. To some extent the same applies to the lower portion of the postcentral gyrus. The supramarginal and angular gyri are located respectively around the terminal parts of the posterior branch of the lateral sulcus and the superior temporal sulcus. The cortex of the angular gyrus is important because it is involved in relating visual impressions to stereognostic impressions (appreciation of the nature of an object by means of touch). Two temporal sulci divide the temporal lobe into three temporal gyri. Along its superior margin the superior temporal gyrus is continued without interruption into the transverse temporal gyrus, these areas of cortex being receiving and processing regions for auditory sensations.

1. Superior frontal gyrus.
2. Superior frontal sulcus.
3. Central sulcus.
4. Precentral gyrus.
5. Postcentral gyrus.
6. Supramarginal gyrus.
7. Angular gyrus.
8. Postcentral sulcus.
9. Parieto-occipital sulcus.
10. Superior parietal lobule.
11. Intraparietal sulcus.
12. Precentral sulcus.
13. Middle frontal gyrus.
14. Inferior frontal sulcus.
15. Inferior frontal gyrus.
16. Ascending ramus of lateral sulcus.
17. Transverse temporal gyrus.
18. Anterior ramus of lateral sulcus.
19. Superior temporal gyrus.
20. Superior temporal sulcus.
21. Middle temporal gyrus.
22. Stem of lateral sulcus.
23. Inferior temporal sulcus.
24. Inferior temporal gyrus.
25. Preoccipital notch.
26. Posterior branch of lateral sulcus.
27. Triangular part of inferior frontal gyrus.
28. Opercular part of inferior frontal gyrus.

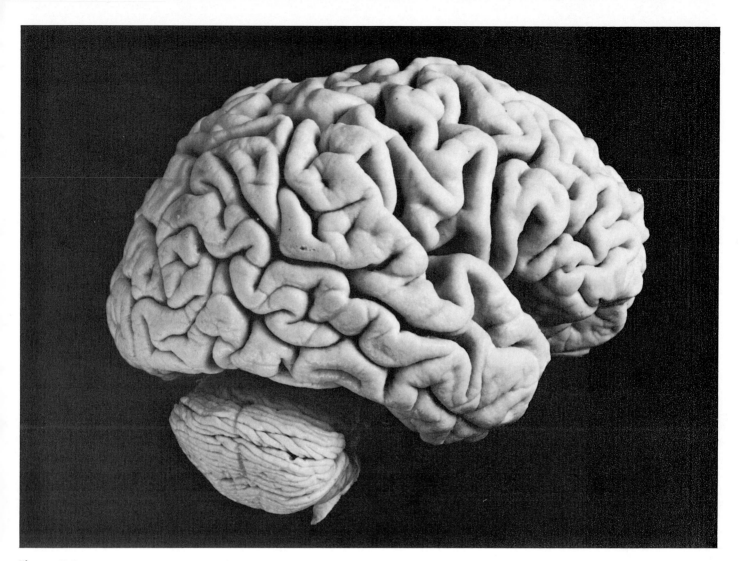

Figure 5-2.

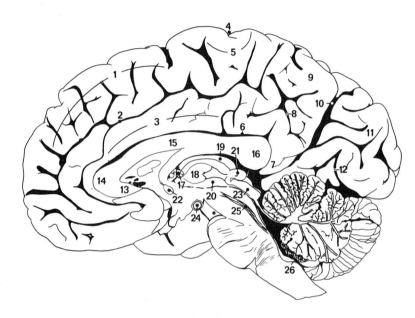

The cingulate sulcus begins below the rostrum of the corpus callosum and arches in front of the genu of the corpus callosum, about a finger's breadth distant from it. Above the splenium of the corpus callosum, the cingulate sulcus turns abruptly to reach the superior margin of the hemisphere.

The central sulcus cuts into the paracentral lobule, where the precentral and postcentral gyri come together. Voluntary control over defecation and micturition reflexes is ascribed to this lobule.

The cingulate gyrus is a long strip of cortex that curves around the corpus callosum. Posteriorly, it becomes very narrow under the splenium of the corpus callosum and is continuous with the isthmus, which separates the splenium from the calcarine sulcus. The cingulate gyrus has profuse reciprocal connections with the anterior thalamic nuclei and is an important constituent of the limbic system. Note the deep parieto-occipital sulcus, running downwards and forwards to the calcarine sulcus. The cuneus is a wedge of cortex enclosed by the parieto-occipital and calcarine sulci and the superomedial margin of the hemisphere. It contains part of the center for sight.

In the brainstem, the medial longitudinal fasciculus is a well-defined white bundle, descending through the midbrain tegmentum, adjacent to the central gray matter. As it approaches the pontine region it gradually adopts a more dorsal position.

1. Medial frontal gyrus.
2. Cingulate sulcus.
3. Cingulate gyrus.
4. Central sulcus.
5. Paracentral lobule.
6. Callosal sulcus.
7. Isthmus of cingulate gyrus.
8. Subparietal sulcus.
9. Precuneus.
10. Parieto-occipital sulcus.
11. Cuneus.
12. Calcarine sulcus.
13. Rostrum of corpus callosum.
14. Genu of corpus callosum.
15. Trunk of corpus callosum.
16. Splenium of corpus callosum.
17. Choroid plexus in interventricular foramen.
18. Interthalamic adhesion.
19. Habenular trigone.
20. Hypothalamic sulcus.
21. Pineal body.
22. Anterior (rostral) commissure.
23. Tectum of midbrain.
24. Mamillary body.
25. Medial longitudinal fascicle.
26. Choroid plexus of 4th ventricle.

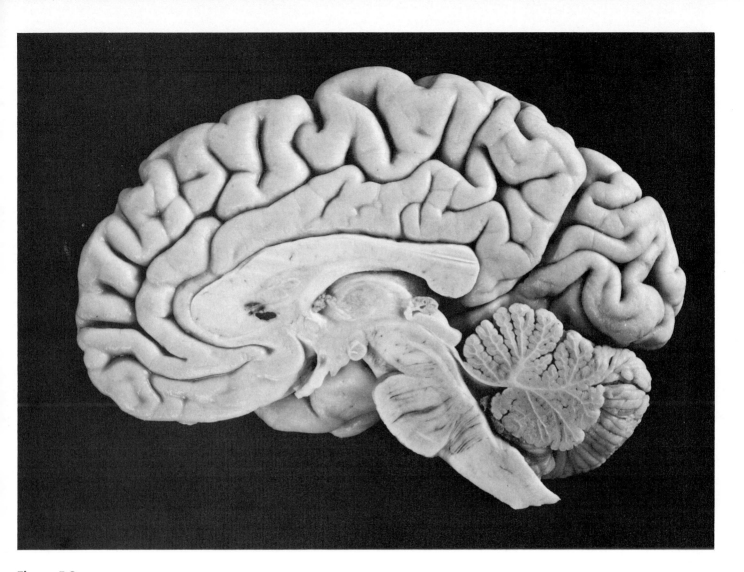

Figure 5-3.

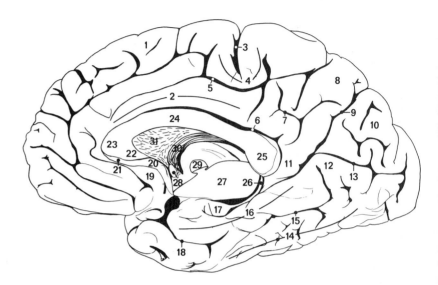

Most of this surface is separated from the left hemisphere by the falx cerebri (dura mater), but the subcallosal area (which is below the rostrum of the corpus callosum) is separated from that of the other side by pia-arachnoid only so that the gyri of the two sides may interlock. The anterior part of the cingulate sulcus is somewhat foreshortened and narrow in this specimen, with a corresponding increase in the paracentral lobule. The paracentral lobule is cut very deeply by the central sulcus (of Rolando). The motor and sensory areas for the lower part of the left lower limb are anterior and posterior to this segment of the central sulcus.

The paraterminal gyrus is closely applied to the anterior surface of the lamina terminalis, and is separated from the cingulate gyrus by a shallow furrow. Primitive in its cytoarchitecture, the thin cortex of the paraterminal gyrus extends on to the inferior surface of the rostrum of the corpus callosum, spreading out to form part of the indusium griseum, which is present also on the superior surface of the corpus callosum and is widely regarded as a primitive cortex and a hippocampal vestige. Beneath the splenium of the corpus callosum, the parahippocampal gyrus bifurcates. The upper part extends over the isthmus to become the cingulate gyrus. The lower part expands backwards to become the lingual gyrus, which is the cortical area below the calcarine sulcus. The posterior part of the calcarine sulcus has been referred to as an "axial sulcus" because it runs longitudinally through the visual striate area and its margins contain much of the center for sight. The anterior part of the calcarine sulcus, after it has been joined by the parieto-occipital sulcus, has been referred to as a "limiting sulcus," because it separates the visual striate area from the cortex of the cingulate gyrus, which is believed to function in emotion.

1. Medial frontal gyrus.
2. Cingulate gyrus.
3. Central sulcus.
4. Paracentral lobule.
5. Cingulate sulcus.
6. Callosal sulcus.
7. Subparietal sulcus.
8. Precuneus.
9. Parieto-occipital sulcus.
10. Cuneus.
11. Isthmus of cingulate gyrus.
12. Lingual gyrus.
13. Calcarine sulcus.
14. Medial occipitotemporal gyrus.
15. Collateral sulcus.
16. Parahippocampal gyrus.
17. Uncus of parahippocampal gyrus.
18. Rhinal sulcus.
19. Subcallosal area.
20. Paraterminal gyrus.
21. Indusium griseum.
22. Rostrum of corpus callosum.
23. Genu of corpus callosum.
24. Trunk of corpus callosum.
25. Splenium of corpus callosum.
26. Fimbria of hippocampus.
27. Cut surface of thalamus.
28. Anterior (rostral) commissure.
29. Interthalamic adhesion.
30. Column of fornix.
31. Septum pellucidum.

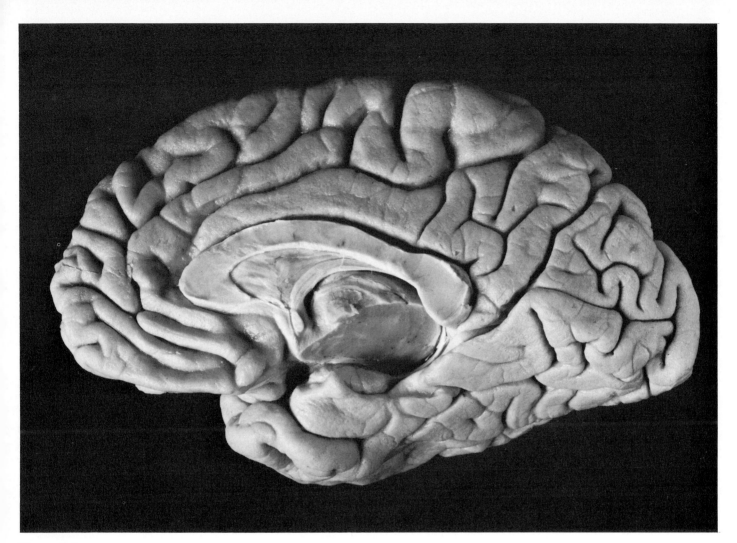

Figure 5-4.

Inferior surface of the brain with cranial nerve attachments, after removal of meninges and superficial blood vessels

The slightly concave inferior surfaces of the frontal lobes rest on the floor of the anterior cranial fossa. The irregularly arranged orbital gyri and sulci include well-developed olfactory gyri, which adjoin the anterior (rostral) perforated substance. There is a clear view of the temporal lobes with their characteristic convolutional pattern. The center and posterior portions of the preparation are occupied by the ventral surfaces of the brain stem and cerebellum, respectively. Note the large bundles of pyramidal fibers decussating within the anterior median fissure.

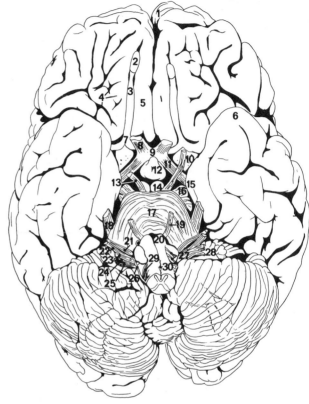

6. Temporal pole of left cerebral hemisphere.
7. Olfactory trigone.
8. Optic nerve.
9. Optic chiasma.
10. Anterior (rostral) perforated substance.
11. Optic tract.
12. Tuber cinereum with infundibulum.
13. Oculomotor nerve.
14. Mamillary body.
15. Uncus of parahippocampal gyrus.
16. Basis pedunculi.
17. Basilar sulcus of pons.
18. Trigeminal nerve.
19. Abducens nerve.
20. Pyramid of medulla oblongata.
21. Facial nerve.
22. Vestibulocochlear nerve.
23. Glossopharyngeal nerve.
24. Vagus nerve.
25. Cranial roots of accessory nerve.
26. Spinal roots of accessory nerve.
27. Rootlets of hypoglossal nerve.
28. Flocculus.
29. Ventral rootlets of 1st cervical spinal nerve.
30. Pyramidal decussation.

1. Frontal pole of left cerebral hemisphere.
2. Olfactory bulb.
3. Olfactory tract.
4. Orbital sulci and gyri.
5. Straight gyrus.

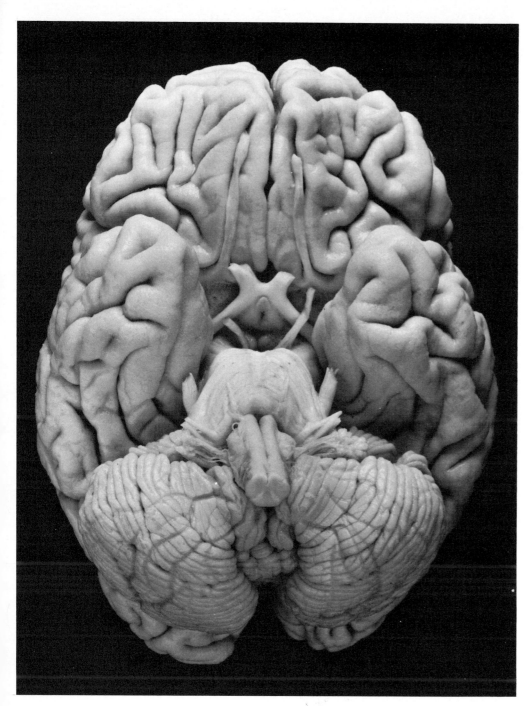

Figure 5-5.

5-6 Inferior surface of the brain after transection through lower midbrain and removal of cerebellum

The brainstem has been cut through the inferior (caudal) colliculi and the decussation of the superior (cranial) cerebellar peduncles. The inferior surfaces of the frontal lobes are separated from those of the temporal lobes by the lateral fissure. On each side, the gyrus rectus of the frontal lobe is well developed and the orbital gyri are arranged irregularly around an H-shaped orbital sulci. The parahippocampal gyri are separated laterally from the rest of the temporal lobe by the collateral sulci, and their medial margins bound the midbrain. The rhinal sulcus is not present as a separate sulcus in this specimen, but is represented as a direct continuation of the collateral sulcus. The rhinal sulcus and the anterior part of the collateral sulcus separate olfactory and paleocortical areas on their medial side from neocortical regions of the temporal cortex on their lateral side. The parahippocampal gyrus continues backwards uninterrupted into the lingual gyrus. The isthmus of the cingulate gyrus is seen as a continuation of the parahippocampal gyrus only in the left hemisphere in this figure, where a small part of the isthmus projects inferior to the splenium of the corpus callosum.

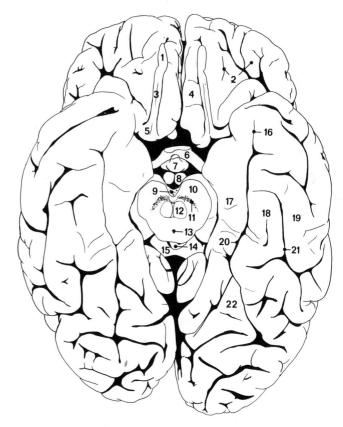

1. Olfactory bulb.
2. Orbital sulci and gyri.
3. Olfactory tract.
4. Straight gyrus.
5. Olfactory trigone.
6. Optic chiasma.
7. Tuber cinereum with infundibulum.
8. Mamillary body.
9. Posterior (interpeduncular) perforated substance.
10. Basis pedunculi.
11. Substantia nigra.
12. Superior cerebellar peduncle.
13. Mesencephalic (cerebral) aqueduct.
14. Pineal body.
15. Splenium of corpus callosum.
16. Rhinal sulcus.
17. Parahippocampal gyrus.
18. Medial occipitotemporal gyrus.
19. Lateral occipitotemporal gyrus.
20. Collateral sulcus.
21. Occipitotemporal sulcus.
22. Lingual gyrus.

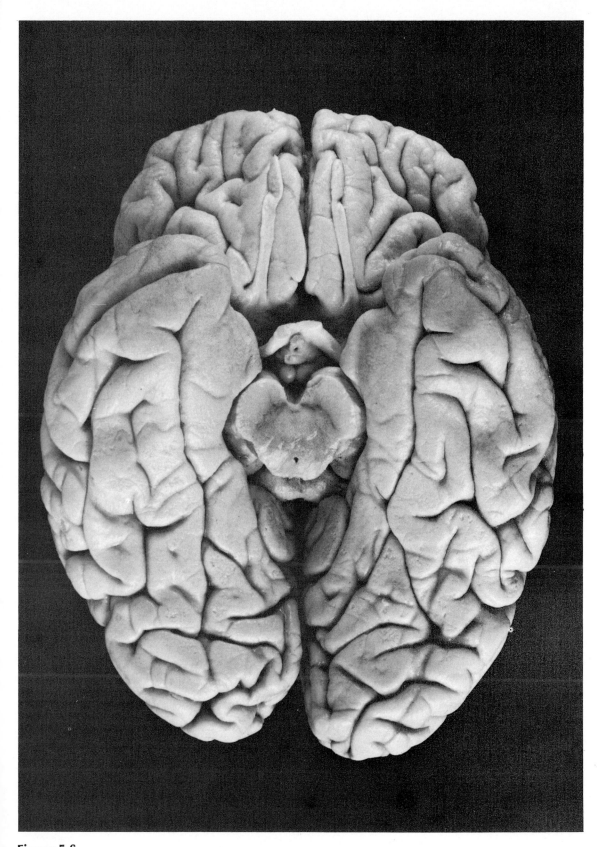

Figure 5-6.

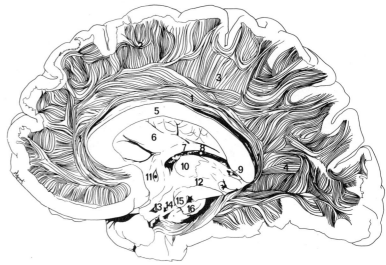

The cingulum is an association tract that commences below the rostrum of the corpus callosum in the region of the olfactory cortex, and arches around the entire corpus callosum. It has been dissected out from the inferior part of the cingulate gyrus in which for the most part it is embedded. After curving round the splenium of the corpus callosum, the bundle proceeds forward within the parahippocampal gyrus to reach the uncus and nearby cortical areas of the temporal lobe. A large proportion of fibers in the cingulum traverse only relatively short segments of this rather compact bundle, and this is due to arrival and departure of many fibers linking different cortical areas. The outer border of the cingulum has a rather irregular appearance. Between the cingulum and the periphery of the specimen, note the mingling of short and long association fibers with commissural and projection fibers.

1. Cingulum.
2. Short arcuate fibres.
3. Projection and commissural fibers.
4. Forceps major or occipital forceps.
5. Corpus callosum.
6. Septum pellucidum.
7. Column of fornix.
8. Tela choroidea of 3rd ventricule.
9. Suprapineal recess.
10. Interthalamic adhesion.
11. Anterior (rostral) commissure.
12. Hypothalamic sulcus.
13. Optic recess.
14. Infundibular recess.
15. Mamillary body.
16. Uncus.

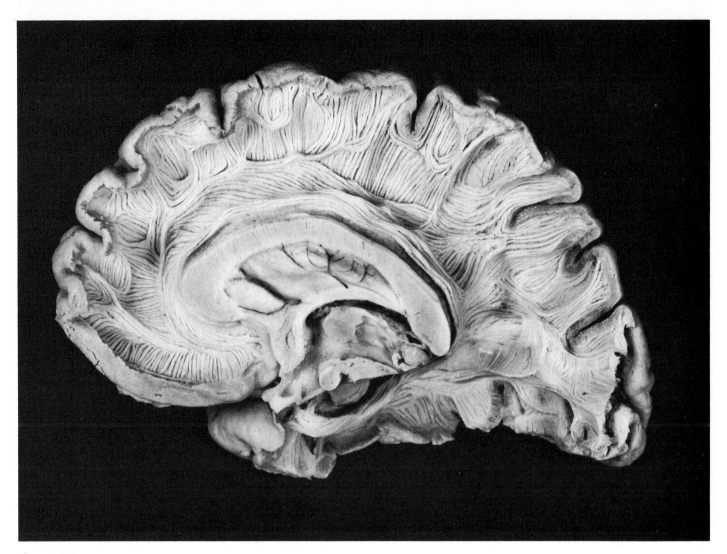

Figure 5-7.

5-8 Caudate nucleus, thalamus and upper brainstem structures: right side of brain, from the medial aspect

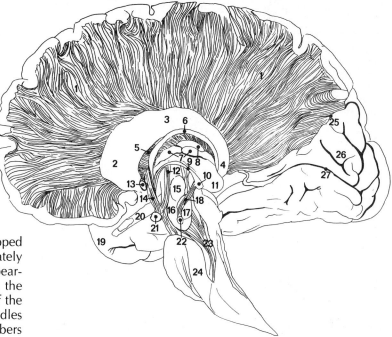

After the ependyma covering its ventricular surface is stripped away, the elongated caudate nucleus is exposed. Immediately above the anterior (rostral) perforated substance, the pear-shaped head of the caudate nucleus is confluent with the putamen of the lentiform nucleus. The lateral surface of the caudate nucleus is in contact with the closely packed bundles of the internal capsule. A well-defined bundle of nerve fibers occupies the furrow between the caudate nucleus and the thalamus. This is the stria terminalis, which arches along the course of the caudate nucleus, closely applied to its medial margin. In its anterior course it diverges slightly from the head of the caudate nucleus, passes beneath the ventral margin of the internal capsule, and—as the main efferent pathway from the amygdaloid nuclear complex—innervates septal nuclei, anterior hypothalamic nuclei, the anterior perforated substance, and the habenular nucleus (via the stria medullaris thalami).

On the stripped dorsal surface of the thalamus, a small portion of the dorsal lateral thalamic nucleus is located most laterally. The anterior nuclear group is situated more medially. Its anterior portion is thickened, and its tapering posterior part sweeps across the dorsal aspect of the thalamus. In partial view only is the medial thalamic nuclei, and (along its medial edge) the stria medullaris. The posterior thalamic nuclei, or pulvinar, project backwards over the superior (cranial) colliculi of the midbrain.

The stria medullaris thalami is prolonged backwards as far as the habenular nuclei, thought to be a center for some olfactory reflexes. The habenulo-interpeduncular tract, the main outflow path from the habenular nuclei, descends across the medial surface of the red nucleus to terminate on the interpeduncular nucleus, situated in the midbrain tegmentum. Anterolateral to the red nucleus is the oval subthalamic nucleus. The darkly pigmented substantia nigra is situated just dorsal to the basis pedunculi. A thin, transversely oriented ribbon of fibers, the medial lemniscus, ascends from the lower brainstem into the midbrain tegmentum where it occupies a ventrolateral position.

The column of the fornix has been divided a short distance above the anterior (ventral) commissure. The fibers of the

1. Corona radiata.
2. Head of caudate nucleus.
3. Body of caudate nucleus.
4. Tail of caudate nucleus.
5. Anterior thalamic peduncle.
6. Stria terminalis.
7. Anterior thalamic nuclear group.
8. Dorsal lateral thalamic nucleus.
9. Stria medullaris thalami.
10. Habenular nucleus.
11. Pulvinar of thalamus.
12. Mamillothalamic fascicle.
13. Anterior (rostral) commissure.
14. Column of fornix.
15. Hypothalamic nuclei
16. Substantia nigra.
17. Red nucleus.
18. Habenulo-interpeduncular tract.
19. Temporal pole.
20. Optic tract.
21. Mamillary body.
22. Interpeduncular nucleus.
23. Medial lemniscus.
24. Median section of pons.
25. Lower lip of parieto-occipital sulcus.
26. Cuneus.
27. Calcarine sulcus.

mamillothalamic fasciculus (bundle of Vicq d' Azyr) arise from the mamillary body and travel upwards and backwards to the anterior, expanded part of the anterior nuclear group of the thalamus.

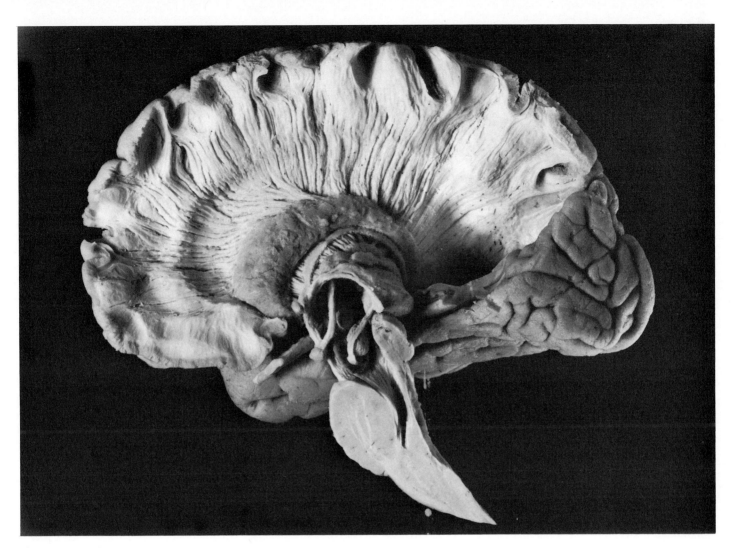

Figure 5-8.

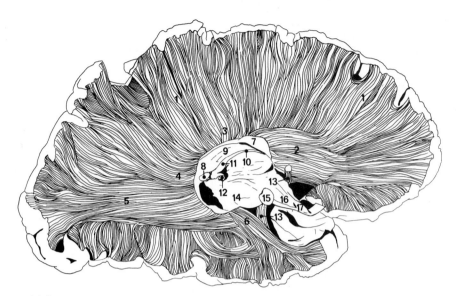

The thalamus is an important integrating center which receives sensory signals of various modalities, and transmits impressions to appropriate areas of the cerebral cortex. In this preparation the corpus callosum, caudate nucleus, and most brainstem structures have been removed. The thalamus is large and gray, and the constituent nuclei on its medial aspect are displayed. The anterior nuclear group of the thalamus arches across the dorsal thalamic surface and consists of the expanded anterior part and a narrow, attenuated posterior part, or tail. The delicate stria medullaris thalami can be traced backwards between the dorsal and medial surfaces of the thalamus towards the habenular trigone. In addition to the habenular trigone, the following components of the epithalamus can be distinguished: the habenular commissure, the pineal body, and the posterior (epithalamic) commissure. The posterior thalamic nucleus, known as the pulvinar, has been excised in part. Normally it juts out backwards over the superior colliculi of the midbrain.

An extensive accumulation of axons connecting various thalamic nuclei to practically all cortical areas is seen in fan-like array and this, in three dimensions, reflects the profusion of the thalamic radiations. For descriptive purposes, different parts of the thalamic radiations are grouped into four thalamic peduncles. All known connections between thalamus and cerebral cortex are reciprocal, two-way radiations (thalamocortical and corticothalamic), and they contribute conspicuously in the formation of the internal capsule and corona radiata. Fibers that originate chiefly from the medial and anterior thalamic nuclei produce the anterior thalamic peduncle, which runs towards anterior and inferior frontal cortical areas. Axons of the superior thalamic peduncle run more or less vertically to connect the thalamus with posterior frontal and parietal cortical areas. The posterior thalamic peduncle and the optic radiation plunge backwards

1. Corona radiata.
2. Anterior thalamic peduncle.
3. Superior thalamic peduncle.
4. Posterior thalamic peduncle.
5. Sagittal stratum.
6. Inferior (caudal) thalamic peduncle.
7. Anterior thalamic nuclear group.
8. Pineal body.
9. Medial thalamic nucleus.
10. Stria medullaris thalami.
11. Habenular trigone.
12. Posterior (epithalamic) commissure.
13. Anterior (rostral) commissure.
14. Cut surface of thalamus.
15. Mamillary body.
16. Tuber cinereum.
17. Optic chiasma.

together in a parasagitally oriented stratum of axons that joins the thalamus to occipital and inferior parietal areas of cortex. The fibers designated as the inferior thalamic peduncle follow a ventrolaterally oriented course towards the temporal lobe cortex. Fibers of the auditory radiation, which originate in the medial geniculate body and travel to the transverse temporal gyri, share with thalamotemporal and temporothalamic fibers in the formation of this peduncle. The temporal genu of the optic radiation is situated lateral to the inferior thalamic peduncle. The latter intersects various projection and commissural fibers, including those crossing to the opposite hemisphere in the anterior commissure.

Figure 5-9.

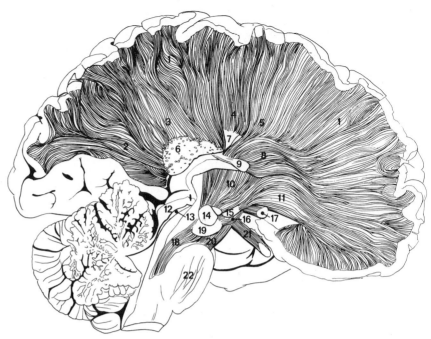

Components of the corona radiata and internal capsule are displayed, showing the convergence of corticofugal fibers as they descend to brainstem levels. Almost the entire corpus callosum with its radiation has been removed. The splenium and a small part of the body are all that is left of the massive callosal system of commissural fibers. From the splenium, commissural fibers radiate towards the cortex, interdigitating with both projection and association fiber bundles. A compact bundle of fibers from the splenium sweeps backwards into the occipital lobe, forming the left half of the occipital forceps. In front of and below the splenium is a small part of the body of the caudate nucleus, which receives an input of corticostriate fibers. More anterior and somewhat more deeply placed are bundles of the massive thalamic radiations, which have a particularly large component that links the thalamus to the sensory cortical areas in the postcentral gyrus.

Removal of the medial and part of the lateral thalamic nuclei has exposed a stalk of corticorubral fibers, converging upon the red nucleus from many cortical areas, including the frontal regions. The red nucleus has been cleaned so that its larger, spherical mesencephalic part can be distinguished from the more rostral, ovoid diencephalic part. Rostral and lateral to the red nucleus is the subthalamic nucleus which also possesses profuse cortical connections. Ventrolateral to the red nucleus and subthalamic nucleus is the substantia nigra, which is a thin, curved sheet of darkly pigmented tissue. The adjoining ventral region of the midbrain is represented by the basis pedunculi packed with groups of corticofugal fibers. Some of these white myelinated fiber bundles can be followed downwards through the ventral part of the pons. Ascending from the medulla and curving dorsolaterally into the tegmentum of the midbrain is the medial lemniscus, on its way to the thalamus.

1. Corona radiata.
2. Occipital forceps.
3. Radiation of corpus callosum.
4. Corticostriate fibers.
5. Superior thalamic peduncle.
6. Splenium of corpus callosum.
7. Body of caudate nucleus.
8. Anterior thalamic peduncle.
9. Anterior thalamic nuclear group.
10. Corticorubral tract.
11. Corticohypothalamic tract.
12. Tectum of midbrain.
13. Mesencephalic (cerebral) aqueduct.
14. Red nucleus.
15. Subthalamic nucleus.
16. Corticonigral tract.
17. Anterior (rostral) commissure.
18. Medial lemniscus.
19. Substantia nigra.
20. Basis pedunculi.
21. Optic tract.
22. Sagittal section of pons.

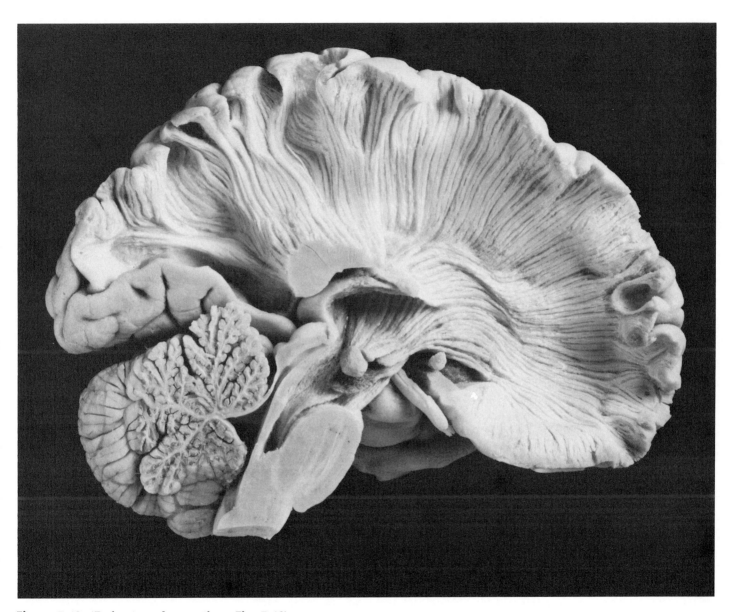

Figure 5-10. (Refer to color section, Fig. 5-10)

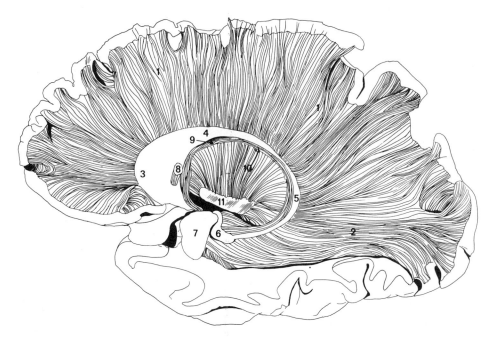

The parts of the caudate nucleus and the amygdaloid body appear in relief after removal of the corpus callosum and brain stem. The striking rounded head of the caudate nucleus extends downwards and, immediately above the anterior (rostral) perforated substance, its gray matter continues uninterrupted as the putamen of the lentiform nucleus, which is concealed from view by the internal capsule. The body and tail of the caudate nucleus form an incomplete circle, the end of the tail widening as it sweeps forwards, into a footlike expansion that attaches to the amygdaloid body anteriorly and the putamen of the lentiform nucleus laterally. A ribbon of white fibers emerges from the posterior aspect of the amygdaloid body, and from the conjoined footlike expansion of the caudate tail. This ribbon becomes consolidated into a bundle of fibers—the stria terminalis—which is the main efferent pathway from the amygdaloid nuclear complex. The stria terminalis runs continuously alongside the medial border of the caudate nucleus, from tail to head. On approaching the anterior (rostral) commissure, the stria terminalis acquires a succession of small patches of gray matter (presumably the bed nucleus of the stria terminalis). The main, postcommissural part of the stria terminalis descends in the direction of the anterior (rostral) perforated substance and ends in parts of the hypothalamus.

1. Corona radiata.
2. Sagittal stratum.
3. Head of caudate nucleus.
4. Body of caudate nucleus.
5. Tail of caudate nucleus.
6. Connecting piece between lentiform nucleus and tail of caudate nucleus.
7. Amygdaloid nuclear complex.
8. Anterior (rostral) commissure.
9. Stria terminalis.
10. Internal capsule.
11. Cut surface of basis pedunculi.

Figure 5-11. (Refer to color section, Fig. 5-11)

5-12 Corona radiata, internal capsule and basis pedunculi arising from the left cerebral hemisphere

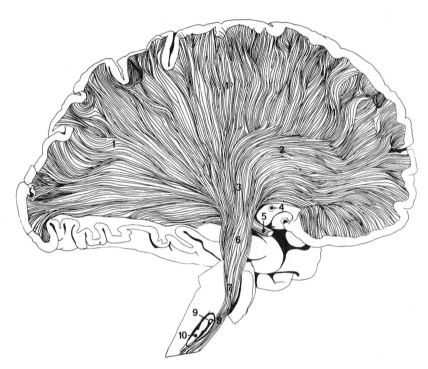

The internal capsule and corona radiata have been exposed by removal of the corpus callosum, caudate nucleus, and diencephalon. The most striking feature of this preparation is the convergence of great masses of corticofugal fibers from extensive areas of cerebral cortex into the relatively narrow, but thick, basis pedunculi. Some torn fibers of the thalamic radiation can still be identified. At the anterior margin of the pons, groups of fibers from the frontal, parietal, occipital, and temporal lobes (corticopontine fibers), which traverse the medial and lateral parts of the basis, terminate in the pontine nuclei; most of the intermediate fibers of the crus (corticospinal and corticonuclear fibers) continue through the ventral part of the pons and medulla oblongata, giving off fibers that synapse in cranial nerve motor nuclei, and into the spinal cord as the corticospinal tracts. In the medulla, note the elongated gray olivary nucleus, with its slitlike hilus, directed dorsomedially. The olivary nucleus is larger and rounded at its upper end, whereas its lower portion is attenuated. The corrugated surface of the olivary nucleus is not apparent when viewed from this aspect.

1. Corona radiata.
2. Torn fibers of anterior thalamic peduncle.
3. Internal capsule.
4. Anterior commissure.
5. Optic tract.
6. Basis pedunculi.
7. Longitudinal pontine fibers (corticospinal and corticonuclear tracts).
8. Pyramidal tract of medulla oblongata.
9. Hilus of olivary nucleus.
10. Olivary nucleus.

Figure 5-12.

5-13　Insula of right cerebral hemisphere

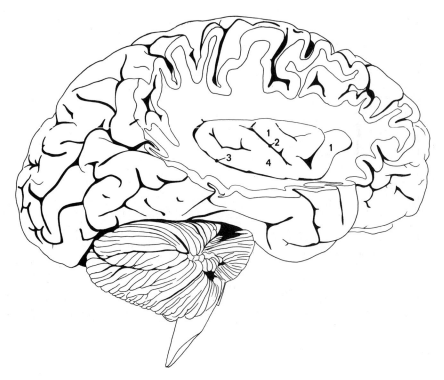

The insula is a substantial portion of cerebral cortex that forms the floor of a fossa that can be opened up by removing the lips bounding the lateral sulcus and its rami. These lips are known as the frontal, frontoparietal and temporal opercula. After their excision, the insula appears as a triangular eminence that is marked by a number of sulci and gyri. The so-called circular sulcus surrounds the insula, except inferomedially where the cortex of the insula is continuous, at the limen insulae, with the cerebral cortex lateral to the anterior (rostral) perforated substance on the basal aspect of the brain. The insular cortex is marked by a number of sulci, one of which—the central sulcus of the insula—is deeper and more prominent than the rest. The central sulcus of the insula runs in an upwards and backwards direction, almost parallel to the main cerebral central sulcus that delimits the frontal lobe from the parietal lobe. In front of the central sulcus of the insula, a few short gyri tend to radiate from the vicinity of the limen insulae. Behind the central sulcus one long gyrus is present in this specimen, partially divided near its upper and posterior end by a shallow sulcus.

1. Short gyri of insula.
2. Central sulcus of insula.
3. Circular sulcus of insula.
4. Long gyrus of insula.

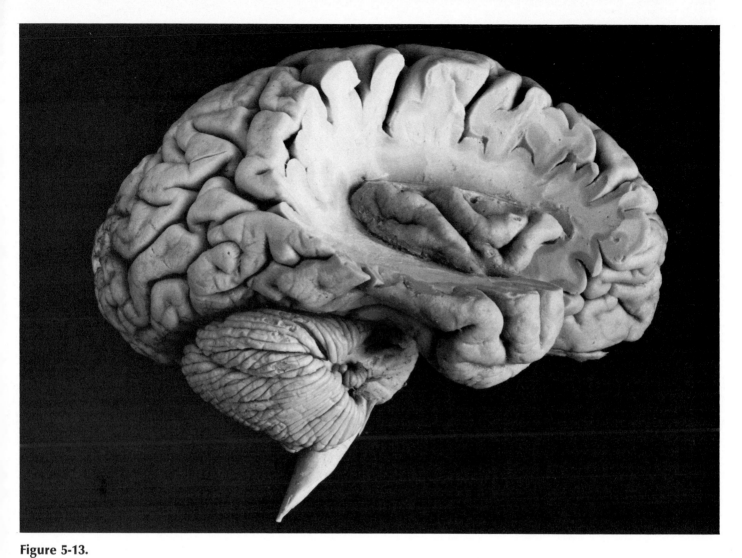

Figure 5-13.

The insular cortex has been exposed by removing the portions of cortex that bound the stem and three rami of the lateral sulcus. It is triangular in shape. The circular sulcus surrounds the insula, except anteroinferiorly where the insular cortex continues uninterrupted via the limen insulae on to the inferior cerebral cortex. The central sulcus of the insula runs upwards and backwards, dividing the cortex into a precentral lobule with short gyri and a postcentral lobule with one or two long gyri.

A thick bundle of long association fibers skirts the upper margin of the insula. This, the superior longitudinal fasciculus, is the largest association bundle, and connects frontal lobe cortex to the occipital and temporal lobes. As it pursues its arched course, the superior longitudinal bundle gathers and sheds nerve fibers from various cortical areas, and so links them to each other. The inferior longitudinal fasciculus, together with the inferior occipitofrontal fasciculus, runs in the inferior part of the hemisphere. It becomes associated with descending fibers of the superior longitudinal fasciculus that, for the most part, end in the occipital cortex. Many arcuate or short association bundles can be seen near the cut margins of the hemisphere. Those connecting neighboring cerebral gyri are clearly seen. Additionally—but not visible in this preparation—short intracortical association fibers exist, linking parts of the same gyrus and sometimes remaining within the cortical gray matter.

1. Short arcuate fibers.
2. Superior longitudinal fascicle.
3. Short gyri of insula.
4. Inferior occipitofrontal fascicle.
5. Central sulcus of insula.
6. Limen of insula.
7. Long gyrus of insula.
8. Inferior longitudinal fascicle.

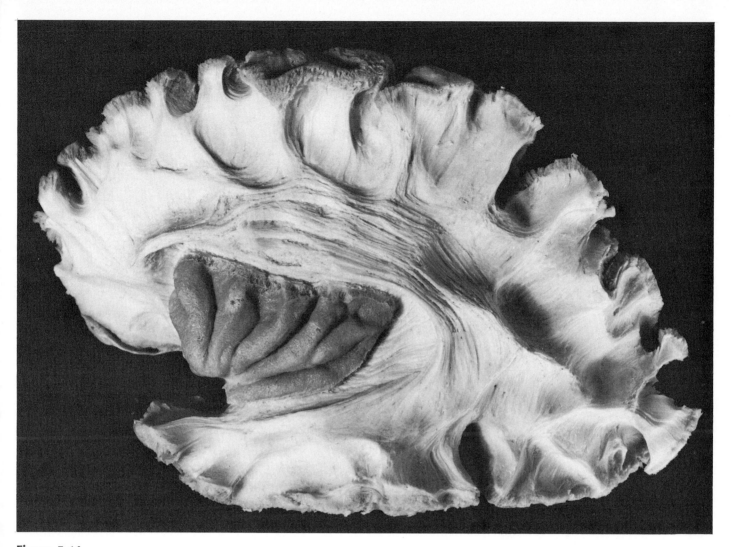

Figure 5-14.

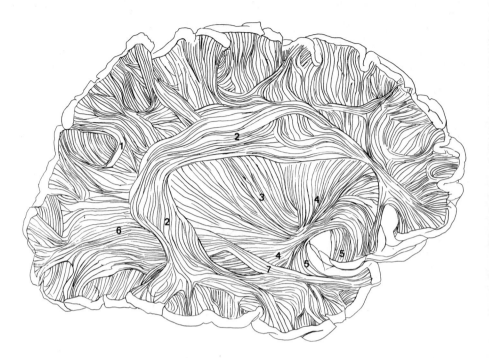

The superior longitudinal fasciculus is composed of fiber bundles of very different lengths. The longer fibers connect the cortical areas far removed from each other, but the majority are somewhat shorter axons that join the fasciculus (in multitudes, from overlying gyri) and mingle with the other fibers of this thick tract. Near the middle of the superior longitudinal fasciculus, some of its fibers—coming from both directions—turn abruptly upwards into the somatomotor and somatosensory areas of the cortex.

The long association fibers of the uncinate fasciculus connect the orbital and inferior frontal gyri of the frontal lobe with the cortex in the anterior part of the temporal lobe, and the fasciculus hooks around the bottom of the stem of the lateral sulcus to do so. The middle portion of the uncinate fasciculus is extensively interconnected with the bulky middle part of the inferior occipitofrontal fasciculus. The latter fans out in both directions, on the one hand radiating towards the frontal and parietal lobes, and on the other streaming into the occipital and temporal lobes. The posterior part of the inferior occipitofrontal fasciculus joins the inferior longitudinal fasciculus, and then both of them intermingle with the descending part of the superior longitudinal fasciculus. In this way is formed the lateral part of a vast stratum of white matter that connects the whole of the occipital cortex with the rest of the brain.

Close to the perimeter of the hemisphere, many bundles of short association, or arcuate, fibers run into the white matter where they intersect and exchange axons with long as well as other short association bundles. This intersecting and mingling is characteristic of association bundles, and contrasts with the orderly formation of projection tracts found in the internal capsule and crus cerebri.

1. Short arcuate fibers.
2. Superior longitudinal fascicle.
3. External capsule.
4. Inferior occipitofrontal fascicle.
5. Uncinate fascicle.
6. Sagittal stratum.
7. Inferior longitudinal fasciculus.

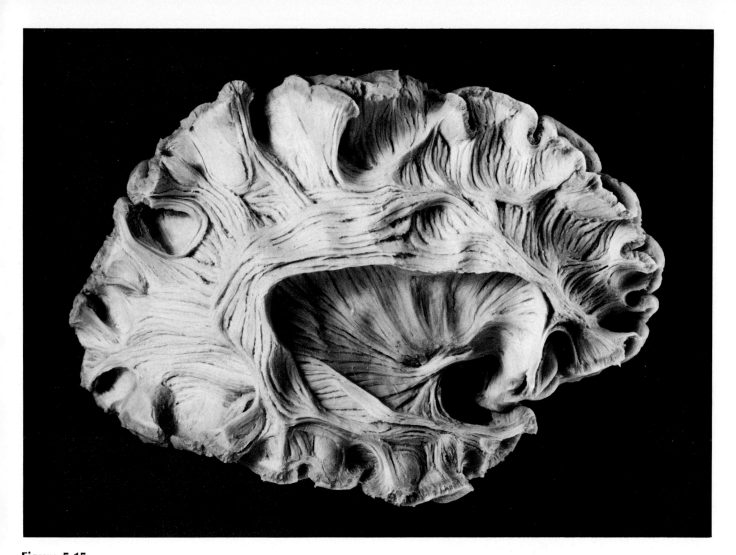

Figure 5-15.

The long association bundles and external capsule have been removed to display the lateral aspect of the putamen, which appears as a dark gray oval mass with a slightly concave ventral margin. It is highly vascular, and the relatively large anterolateral and posterolateral central arteries (not shown) ascend in grooves over the lower part of the lateral surface of the putamen before piercing successively the lentiform nucleus, internal capsule, and caudate nucleus.

Narrow gray bridges pass between fiber bundles of the internal capsule and connect the putamen to the head and the body of the caudate nucleus, which—except for the bridges—is separated from the putamen by the internal capsule. The anterior (rostral) commissure occupies a deep groove in the lower surface of the putamen. Its fiber bundles are twisted like a thick string. Below the anterior limb of the internal capsule, the most rostral part of the putamen becomes directly continuous with the head of the caudate nucleus.

Internal capsule fibers radiate via the corona radiata to practically all cortical areas. These projection fibers consist largely of ascending fibers of the thalamic radiation and descending corticofugal fibers. They intersect a major population of commissural fibers that have traversed the corpus callosum and, closer to the cortex, they pass between the short association fibers. An extensive sheet of sagittally running fibers extends posteriorly and includes fibers of the posterior thalamic peduncle, anterior (rostral) commissure, and optic radiation.

1. Corona radiata.
2. Putamen.
3. Gray connections between putamen and caudate nucleus.
4. Sagittal stratum.
5. Anterior (rostral) commissure.

Figure 5-16.

Globus pallidus of lentiform nucleus, internal capsule, and corona radiata: left hemisphere from the lateral aspect

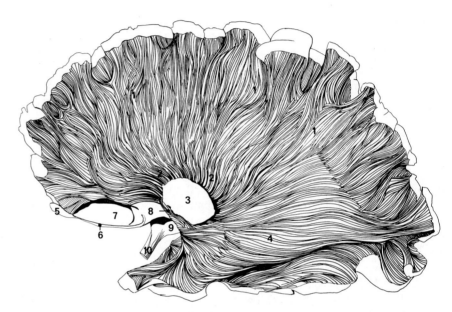

The putamen of the lentiform nucleus has been removed to expose the more medially placed globus pallidus, which receives its name because it is paler than the putamen. The globus pallidus is a nuclear mass which is closely applied to the outer surface of the internal capsule. Just anterior to the globus pallidus, the many narrow grooves between internal capsule fiber bundles were occupied by gray matter joining the putamen (removed) to the head of the caudate nucleus (covered by the anterior limb of the internal capsule). Just ventral to the globus pallidus the anterior (rostral) commissure, which is composed of twisted fiber bundles, intersects fibers of the optic radiation, before the commissural axons stream into the temporal and occipital lobes.

The corona radiata and its continuity with the internal capsule can be seen in this dissection, since the ends and upper margin of the putamen mark the junction of the internal capsule with the base of the corona. From this base, projection fiber bundles diverge towards cortical areas and intersect with commissural fibers of the corpus callosum. Near the periphery of the hemisphere there is also an intermingling of projection and commissural fibers with short association fibers. A contrasting appearance is afforded by the long, parallel, closely packed fibers of the sagittal stratum, the fibers of which remain rather discrete as they pursue their long and wavy course towards the occipital cortex.

1. Corona radiata.
2. Internal capsule.
3. Globus pallidus.
4. Sagittal stratum.
5. Olfactory bulb.
6. Olfactory tract.
7. Straight gyrus.
8. Anterior (rostral) commissure.
9. Optic chiasma.
10. Optic nerve.

Figure 5-17.

Examples of the three major classes of axon (projection, commissural, and association) in the white matter of the brain are seen here. A multitude of **projection** fibers are gathered together in the corona radiata, and can be followed as they converge and continue without interruption in the internal capsule and the basis pedunculi. The constituent parts (putamen and globus pallidus) of the lentiform nucleus have been removed, providing better exposure of the anterior (rostral) commissure seen in the lower part of the preparation. These **commissural** fibers connect parts of the cortex of the two hemispheres, in particular, the anterior and inferior portions of the temporal lobes.

Two **association** tracts are also displayed. The rounded bundle known as the uncinate fasciculus is named for its hooklike configuration as it curves beneath the stem of the lateral sulcus to connect areas of cortex in the lower frontal and anterior temporal regions. The long association fibers of the inferior occipitofrontal fasciculus mingle with the internal capsule and the corona radiata, and also with the anterior commissure and the temporal genu of the optic radiation.

The vertical extent of the inferior occipitofrontal fasciculus is considerable, and it is a major component of the sagittal stratum (which is a fiber sheet of great complexity). The sagittal stratum contains **commissural** fibers that have crossed from the opposite side of the anterior commissure, **association** fibers that extend anteroposteriorly in the inferior occipitofrontal fasciculus, and **projection** fibers belonging to the posterior thalamic peduncle, the optic radiation and the occipitopontine tract.

1. Corona radiata.
2. Internal capsule.
3. Anterior commissure.
4. Inferior occipitofrontal fasciculus.
5. Uncinate fascicle.
6. Sagittal stratum.

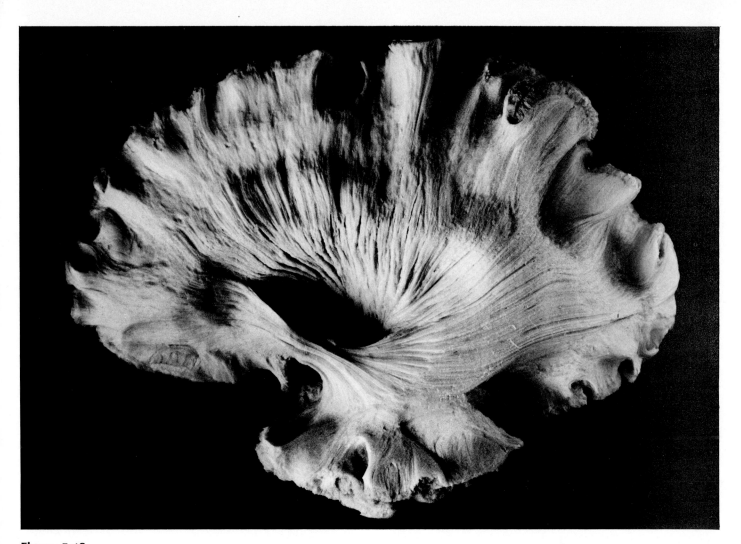

Figure 5-18.

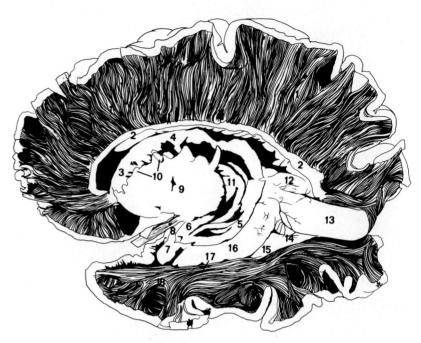

The extreme, external, and internal capsules have been dissected away to show the basal ganglia (caudate and lentiform nuclei and the amygdaloid nuclear complex) which are related to the various parts of the lateral ventricle. The irregular empty spaces between the putamen and the caudate nucleus were occupied by fiber bundles of the internal capsule. Bridges of gray substance pass across the internal capsule, producing the striped appearance from which the corpus striatum derives its name. The gray strands connect the putamen with the head and occasionally the body of the caudate nucleus, reflecting through their conjoined structure in the adult that they arise as a single nuclear mass in development. In the evolutionary process, these neostriatal nuclear masses grow in association with expanding areas of neocortex and the teeming increase in projection fibers converging on the internal capsule. The caudate nucleus has the form of a highly arched comma, and its head, body, and tail are related throughout to the curvature of the lateral ventricle. The pear-shaped head of the caudate nucleus bulges into the floor and lateral wall of the anterior horn, the body of the nucleus is in contact with the floor of the central part of the ventricle, and the tail of the nucleus is located in the roof of the inferior horn, just lateral to the stria terminalis. The gray matter of the tail of the caudate nucleus continues without interruption into the amygdaloid nuclear complex, and also into the gray substance of the lentiform nucleus by way of a small, horizontally placed connecting piece (the "foot of the lentiform nucleus" of earlier workers). The pulvinar of the thalamus can be distinguished just posterior to the putamen.

Commissural fibers in the corpus callosum stream across the roof of the frontal horn and central part of the lateral ventricle. The medial wall of the occipital horn is marked by

1. Corona radiata.
2. Corpus callosum.
3. Head of caudate nucleus.
4. Body of caudate nucleus.
5. Tail of caudate nucleus.
6. "Foot" of lentiform nucleus.
7. Amygdaloid nuclear complex.
8. Optic tract.
9. Putamen.
10. Gray connections between putamen and caudate nucleus.
11. Pulvinar of thalamus.
12. Bulb of occipital horn of lateral ventricle.
13. Calcar avis.
14. Collateral trigone.
15. Collateral eminence.
16. Hippocampus.
17. Inferior longitudinal fasciculus.
18. Short arcuate fibers.

two swellings. The upper one, known as the bulb of the posterior horn, owes its existence to the white matter of the occipital forceps, consisting of fibers that cross in the splenium of the corpus callosum. The lower swelling, the calcar avis, is produced by the calcarine sulcus located on the medial surface of the occipital lobe. The hippocampal sulcus invaginates most of the medial wall of the inferior horn of the lateral ventricle to produce the prominent curved elevation called the hippocampus. The blunt anterior part of the hippocampus (pes hippocampi) possesses characteristic digitations. The collateral eminence and trigone are located in the floor of the inferior and posterior horns, produced by the collateral sulcus.

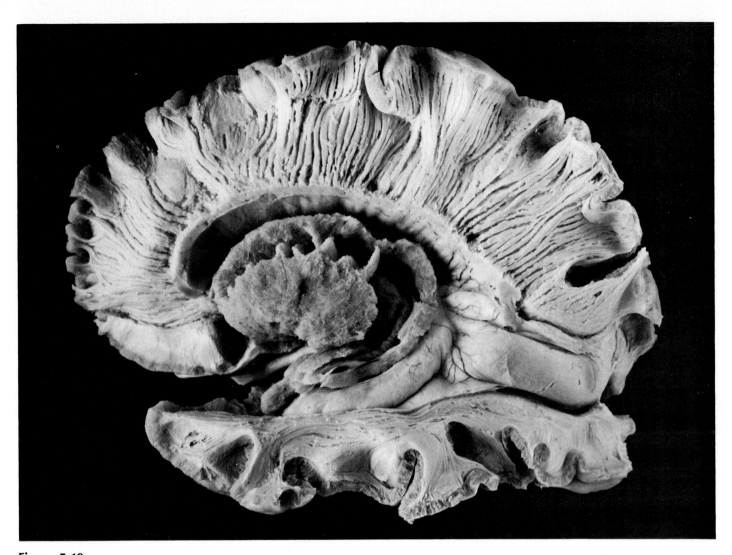

Figure 5-19.

On the right is seen the large, medullary area of the cerebral hemisphere, surrounded by a layer of gray cortical matter. The medullary area is packed with myelinated nerve fibers which are arranged, according to their courses and connections, into commissural, association, and projection fibers. In the cut surface of the right hemisphere are a few bundles of commissural fibers which cross the midline in the corpus callosum.

The left hemisphere has been sliced at a slightly lower level. A rectangular piece of cerebrum adjacent to the midline has been removed to display part of the upper surface of the corpus callosum. The latter is covered by the indusium griseum, a thin sheet of rudimentary cortex containing (on each side) the delicate medial and lateral longitudinal striae. Lateral to the indusium griseum, densely packed, transversely running commissural fibers of the corpus callosum are apparent. In the posterior part of the left hemisphere, the commissural fibers of the splenium of the corpus callosum curve sharply backward to form the left part of the occipital forceps. The upper surface of the left superior temporal gyrus is visible in the floor of the posterior ramus of the lateral sulcus. The superior temporal gyrus is subdivided into two or more obliquely running, short, transverse temporal gyri. The anterior transverse temporal gyrus and the adjacent part of the superior temporal gyrus together constitute the cortical auditory area (subject to individual variation).

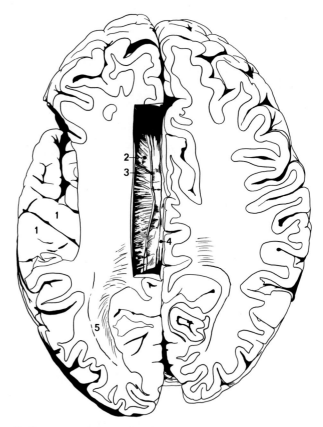

1. Transverse temporal gyri.
2. Commissural callosal fibers.
3. Lateral longitudinal stria.
4. Medial longitudinal stria.
5. Occipital forceps.

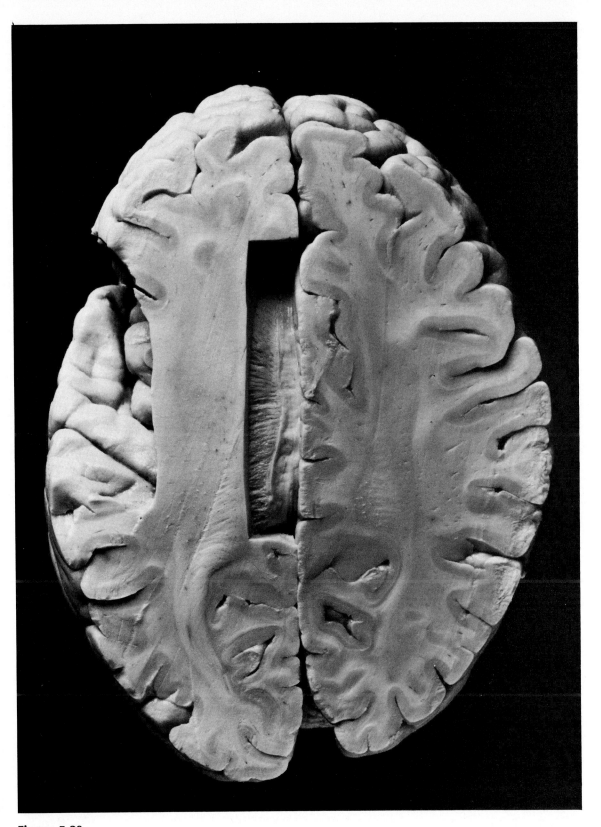

Figure 5-20.

5-21 Corpus callosum, its radiation, and indusium griseum displayed from above

These structures have been exposed by partial removal of the cerebral hemispheres. The trunk, or intermediate, portion of the corpus callosum consists of closely packed bundles of transversely oriented commissural fibers. The anterior and posterior portions of the corpus callosum curve sharply downwards to form its genu and splenium respectively. The commissural fibers traversing the genu and splenium form characteristic arches—the frontal and occipital forceps, respectively—in order to reach the anterior and posterior poles of the hemispheres. Traced laterally, the fibers of the corpus callosum become widely dispersed as they radiate towards the various lobes of the hemispheres, and difficulty is experienced in following callosal fibers more laterally because they interdigitate with association and projection fibers. To display the commissural fibers better, some of the projection fibers have been dissected away, their removal having enlarged the spaces between bundles of callosal fibers.

The upper surface of the intermediate portion of the corpus callosum is covered by a thin veil of gray substance—the indusium griseum. Two pairs of medial and lateral longitudinal white striae are embedded within the gray matter of the indusium, creating four fine ridges. The lateral ridges are somewhat more prominent, and they demarcate the transition between the indusium griseum medially and the gray matter of the cingulate gyrus (which has been removed) laterally.

The corpus callosum and its overlying indusium griseum exhibit striking developmental and functional contrasts. The latter is a thin sheet of gray matter representing a vestigial cerebral convolution and is a residue of the primitive, **archipallial** cortex. The corpus callosum is a typical neocortical development: in man it is a highly developed commissure that connects practically all **neopallial** areas of cortex with one another.

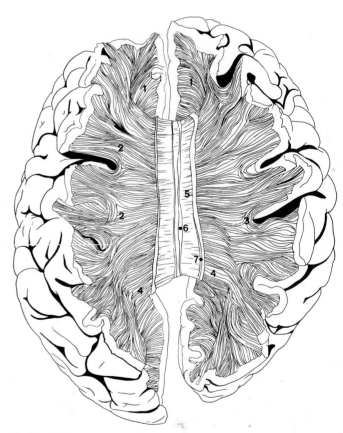

1. Frontal forceps.
2. Commissural callosal fibers.
3. Short arcuate fibers.
4. Occipital forceps.
5. Indusium griseum.
6. Medial longitudinal stria.
7. Lateral longitudinal stria.

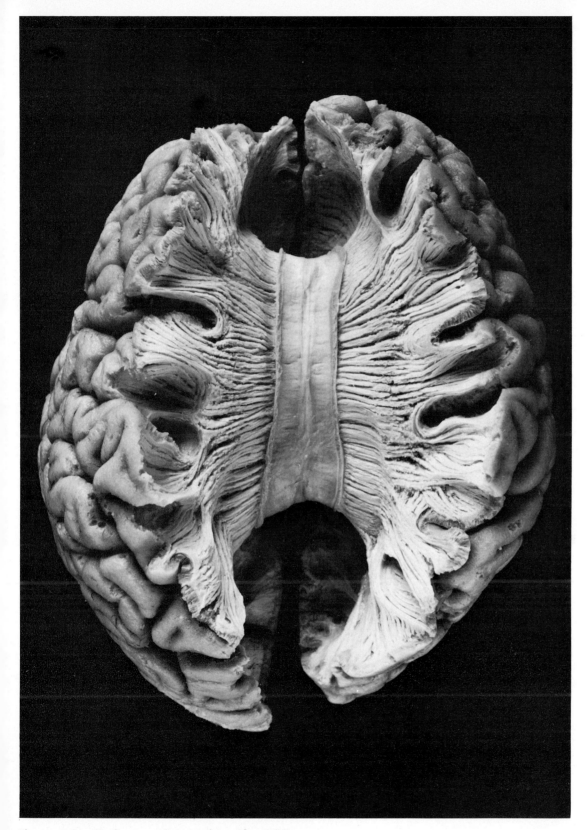

Figure 5-21. (Refer to color section, Fig. 5-21)

A fold of the pia mater enters the brain to produce the tela choroidea of the 3rd ventricle. Arteries carried in with the pial fold provide the choroid plexuses of the 3rd and lateral ventricles. The upper parts of both cerebral hemispheres, the body of the corpus callosum and most of the fornix, have been removed. The tela choroidea of the 3rd ventricle is located immediately below the body of the fornix. It is a double fold of highly vascular pia mater and triangular in outline. Its anterior angle approaches the columns of the fornix, adjacent to the interventricular foramina, and its broad base is beneath the splenium of the corpus callosum. Each lateral margin of the tela choroidea contains the highly vascularized choroid plexus of the body of the corresponding lateral ventricle. Thus the choroid plexuses of the lateral ventricles are in fact only lateral expansions of the tela choroidea of the 3rd ventricle, and they extend into the lateral ventricles by way of the choroid fissures.

The choroid fissure is a potential slit only, located between the fornix and the lamina affixa on the dorsal side of the thalamus. The choroid fissure also follows the curve of the fimbria and the stria terminalis, between which the plexus gains entry into the inferior horn of the lateral ventricle. The choroid plexus of the lateral ventricle therefore continues uninterrupted from the interventricular foramina backwards within the central part of the ventricle. Then, after sweeping round the posterior end of the thalamus, the plexus extends downwards and forwards in the temporal horn of the lateral ventricle. The choroid plexus does not extend into the frontal and occipital horns of the lateral ventricles. The choroid plexus of the 3rd ventricle is much smaller and bulges downward from the tela choroidea into the ventricles.

Each internal cerebral vein is formed at the anterior angle of the tela choroidea by the union of the thalamostriate vein, the choroid vein (which issues from the choroid plexus) and the vein of the septum pellucidum. Numerous tributaries from the thalamus and caudate nucleus converge upon the thalamostriate vein, which is partially obscured by the stria terminalis. The two veins of the septum pellucidum are of small caliber and emerge from between the two laminae of the septum pellucidum. The two internal cerebral veins join under the splenium of the corpus callosum to form the great cerebral vein, but the site of union is not visible in this preparation.

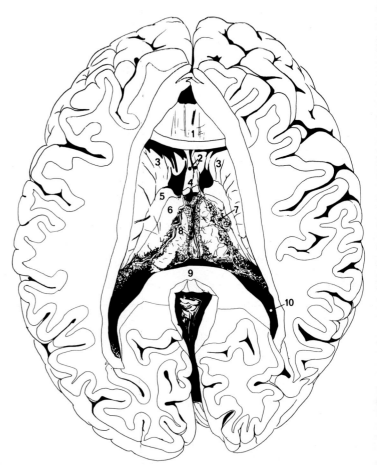

1. Corpus callosum with indusium griseum.
2. Laminae of septum pellucidum.
3. Head of caudate nucleus.
4. Columns of fornix.
5. Stria terminalis.
6. Lamina affixa.
7. Choroid plexus of lateral ventricle.
8. Tela choroidea of 3rd ventricle with choroid plexus and internal cerebral veins.
9. Splenium of corpus callosum.
10. Occipital horn of lateral ventricle.

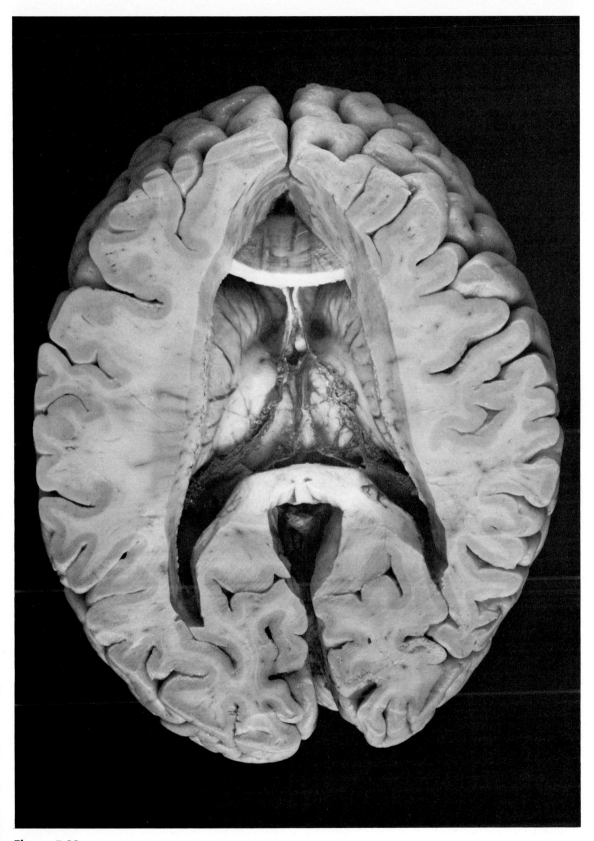

Figure 5-22.

The deep cerebellar nuclei have been dissected out. The large dentate nuclei are deeply fissured and subdivided into tooth-like agglomerations of gray matter, the longest ones being near the middle of each nucleus. From each subdivision arise fine bands of white fibers which together contribute the greater part of the superior cerebellar peduncle. The fastigial nucleus is the most medially placed cerebellar nucleus. It is a small, slightly elongated gray mass situated in the roof of the 4th ventricle. A small fiber bundle issuing from its rostral part runs alongside the medial margin of the superior cerebellar peduncle and then disappears from view (heading for the ipsilateral vestibular nuclear complex and reticular formation). There are two globose nuclei in each cerebellar hemisphere, the anterior one just dorsolateral to the fastigial nucleus and the posterior one attached to the emboliform nucleus. Slender bundles arising from the globose and emboliform nuclei traverse the main part of the superior cerebellar peduncle.

Due to removal of the basis pedunculi, substantia nigra, and the greater part of the midbrain tegmentum, the decussation of the superior cerebellar peduncles can be seen. This decussation occurs in the midbrain tegmentum at the level of the inferior (caudal) colliculi. After crossing, the efferent fibers from these cerebellar nuclei pursue two courses. Many from the globose and emboliform nuclei terminate in the red nucleus, which in this preparation appears as a large, rounded nuclear mass. Fibers predominantly from the contralateral dentate nucleus bypass the red nucleus and head directly for the ventral intermediate thalamic nucleus. It may be noted that the rostral end of the red nucleus receives the substantial corticorubral tract, which is believed to contain an admixture of rubrothalamic fibers.

Lateral to the midbrain are the medial and lateral geniculate bodies. The former is rounded, whereas the lateral geniculate body resembles an inverted cup. The ventrally placed notch in the lateral geniculate body is readily seen, with optic tract fibers terminating on both sides of this deep ventral groove. Lateral to the geniculate bodies, sharply recurved fibers of the optic radiation make their diversion into the temporal lobes. (This is shown to better advantage on the right side of the illustration). A little lateral to the posterior end of the optic tract, the thick, slightly curved, highly vascular putamen is seen with the smaller globus pallidus on its medial side. Fibers of the external capsule and the lateral and medial medullary laminae have been removed to display the putamen and medial and lateral divisions of the globus pallidus.

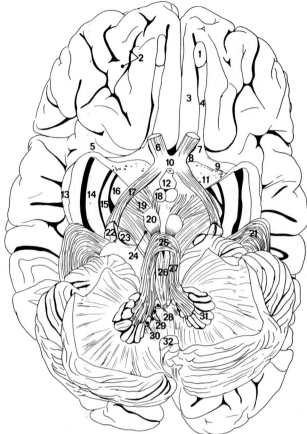

1. Olfactory bulb.
2. Orbital sulci and gyri.
3. Straight gyrus.
4. Olfactory tract.
5. Limen of insula.
6. Optic nerve.
7. Olfactory trigone.
8. Medial olfactory gyrus containing stria.
9. Lateral olfactory gyrus containing stria.
10. Optic chiasma.
11. Anterior (rostral) perforated substance.
12. Tuber cinereum with infundibulum.
13. Long gyrus of insula.
14. Putamen.
15. Lateral part of globus pallidus.
16. Medial part of globus pallidus.
17. Optic tract.
18. Mamillary body.
19. Corticorubral and rubrothalamic tracts.
20. Red nucleus.
21. Optic radiation.
22. Lateral geniculate nucleus.
23. Medial geniculate nucleus.
24. Cerebellothalamic tract.
25. Decussation of superior cerebellar peduncles.
26. Superior medullary velum.
27. Superior cerebellar peduncle.
28. Fastigial nucleus.
29. Globose nuclei.
30. Emboliform nucleus.
31. Dentate nucleus.
32. Vermis.

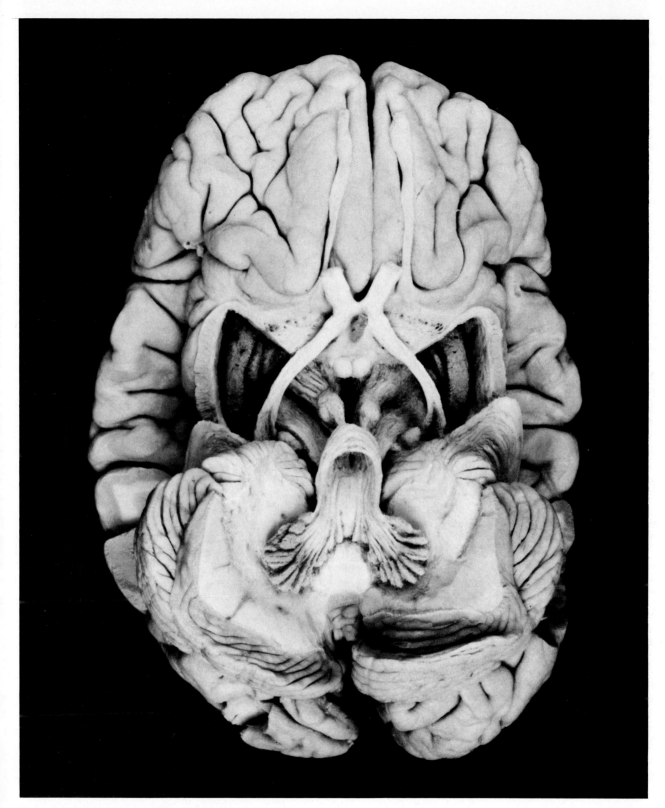

Figure 5-23. (Refer to color section, Fig. 5-23)

5-24 Visual pathway from optic chiasma to occipital lobes, viewed from the basal aspect

Each optic tract can be traced backwards and laterally, its initial segment passing between the anterior (rostral) perforated substance laterally and the tuber cinereum and mamillary body medially. After arching across the basis pedunculi, it terminates in the lateral geniculate body which has a distinct notch in its ventral surface. The larger part of the lateral geniculate body is lateral to this notch, and is responsible for the swelling seen below the pulvinar of the thalamus. The medial part of the lateral geniculate body is commonly confused with the medial root of the optic tract. (The ventral notch in the lateral geniculate body was filled with optic tract fibers and these have been removed to show the nucleus.) Many optic nerve fibers proceed in a medial direction as the brachium of the superior (cranial) colliculus, destined for the pretectal area and the superior (cranial) colliculus.

The fibers of the optic radiation, or geniculostriate projection, emerge from the dorsal surface of the lateral geniculate body and can be traced as part of a sagittal stratum of white fibers that runs forwards and downwards into the temporal lobe. Subsequently, they sweep backwards and terminate in the region of the calcarine sulcus. More dorsally placed fibers of the optic radiation (not seen) pursue a shorter and more direct path to the visual cortex. Note that the anterior (rostral) commissure, and the inferior occipitofrontal fasciculus form, with the optic radiation, the sagittal stratum of white fibers that supplies the occipital cortex with both afferent and efferent connections.

The medial geniculate body is located dorsomedial to the lateral geniculate body. The midbrain has been cut at the level of the inferior (caudal) colliculi. The cut surfaces of the superior cerebellar peduncles are more ventral. Two small white areas found in the dorsal tegmentum are the medial longitudinal fasciculi. On each side, the ventral aspect of the claustrum and the subdivisions of the lentiform nucleus (putamen, medial, and lateral parts of globus pallidus) are seen lateral to the optic tracts. The claustrum is a layer of gray matter that lies on the medial aspect of the insular cortex, from which it is separated by a sheet of white fibers known as the extreme capsule (not displayed here). Only a narrow interval separates the anteroventral parts of these basal ganglia from the anterior (rostral) perforated substance. The medial and lateral olfactory striae define the anterior limit of the anterior perforated substance.

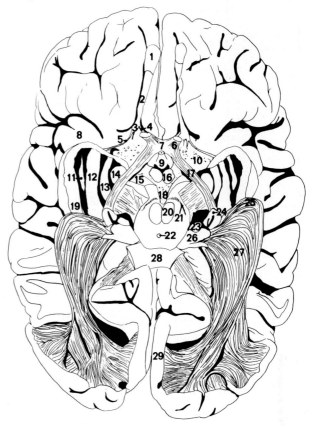

1. Olfactory bulb.
2. Olfactory tract.
3. Olfactory trigone.
4. Medial olfactory stria.
5. Lateral olfactory stria.
6. Optic nerve.
7. Optic chiasma.
8. Limen insulae.
9. Tuber cinereum with infundibulum.
10. Anterior (rostral) perforated substance.
11. Claustrum.
12. Putamen.
13. Lateral part of globus pallidus.
14. Medial part of globus pallidus.
15. Basis pedunculi.
16. Mamillary body.
17. Optic tract.
18. Posterior (interpeduncular) perforated substance.
19. Cortex of insula.
20. Superior cerebellar peduncle.
21. Substantia nigra.
22. Mesencephalic (cerebral) aqueduct.
23. Medial geniculate nucleus.
24. Lateral geniculate nucleus.
25. Temporal genu of optic radiation.
26. Pulvinar of thalamus.
27. Sagittal stratum.
28. Splenium of corpus callosum.
29. Upper lip of calcarine sulcus.

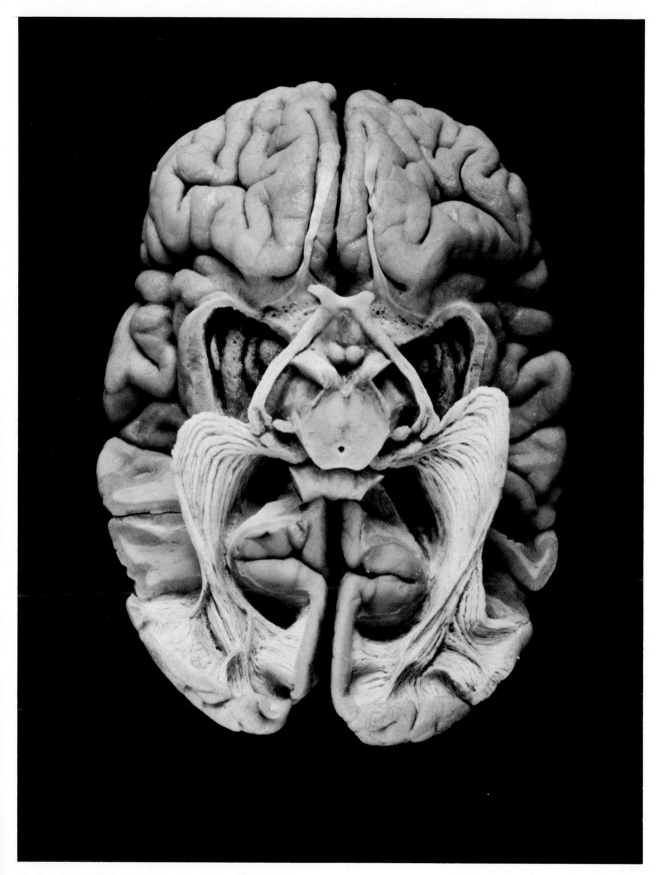

Figure 5-24. (Refer to color section, Fig. 5-24)

The cerebellum, brainstem, thalami, and most of the basal ganglia have been removed. Hippocampal structures can be examined on both sides. The fornix, mamillary bodies, and part of the anterior (rostral) commissure can also be seen.

The two halves of the cerebrum have been dissected from below to different depths, to allow study of the dentate gyrus (left side of illustration) and the upper cortical layer of the parahippocampal gyrus (right side) which covers the inferior aspect of the dentate gyrus. On the right side the superficial gray matter and medullary white substance of the parahippocampal gyrus have been cleaned away to expose cortical substance on the deep aspect of the gyrus. Fine digitations are characteristic of this deep cortical substance. The cut edge of the alveus can also be seen. Note the hook or uncus of the parahippocampal gyrus. On the smooth inferior surface of the uncus is the delicate, transversely running tail of the dentate gyrus that runs into the cleft of the uncus. More anterior is the amygdaloid nuclear complex.

On the left side of the illustration (right side of the specimen), the parahippocampal gyrus has been removed to expose the dentate gyrus. Note the characteristic, toothlike appearance of the inferior surface of the dentate gyrus. Traced backwards around the splenium of the corpus callosum, the dentate gyrus is continuous with the gyrus fasciolaris (or subsplenial gyrus) which continues on the superior surface of the corpus callosum as the indusium griseum. Anteriorly, the dentate gyrus truns abruptly, medially and posteriorly, thereby forming the tail of the dentate gyrus. Two gray elevations located anterior and anteromedial to the tail of the dentate gyrus are parts of the deep cortex of the uncus. Note the broad white sheet of the alveus and, just medial to the dentate gyrus, the fimbria of the hippocampus, a thick white bundle of axons that runs first backwards, then forwards and superiorly to form the highly arched crus of the fornix.

Between the two crura of the fornix is a white, triangular lamina, known as the fornical commissure. Follow the body and the columns of the fornix to observe that most of their fibers travel to the mamillary bodies. Anterior and dorsal to the mamillary bodies, find the transversely oriented cylindrical white band which is the anterior (rostral) commissure. In the depths of the specimen it is possible to see the inferior surface of the corpus callosum, to which the body of the fornix is firmly attached.

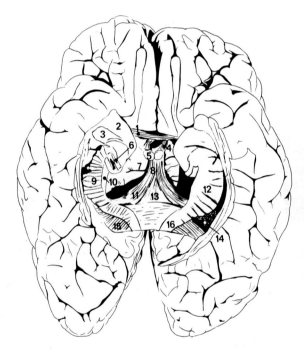

1. Anterior (rostral) commissure.
2. Cut surface of parahippocampal gyrus.
3. Amygdaloid nuclear complex.
4. Column of fornix.
5. Mamillary body.
6. Tail of dentate gyrus.
7. Inferior surface of corpus callosum.
8. Body of fornix.
9. Dentate gyrus.
10. Fimbria of hippocampus.
11. Crus of fornix.
12. Deep cortex of parahippocampal gyrus.
13. Commissure of fornix.
14. Choroid plexus in temporal horn of lateral ventricle.
15. Splenium of corpus callosum.
16. Gyrus fasciolaris.

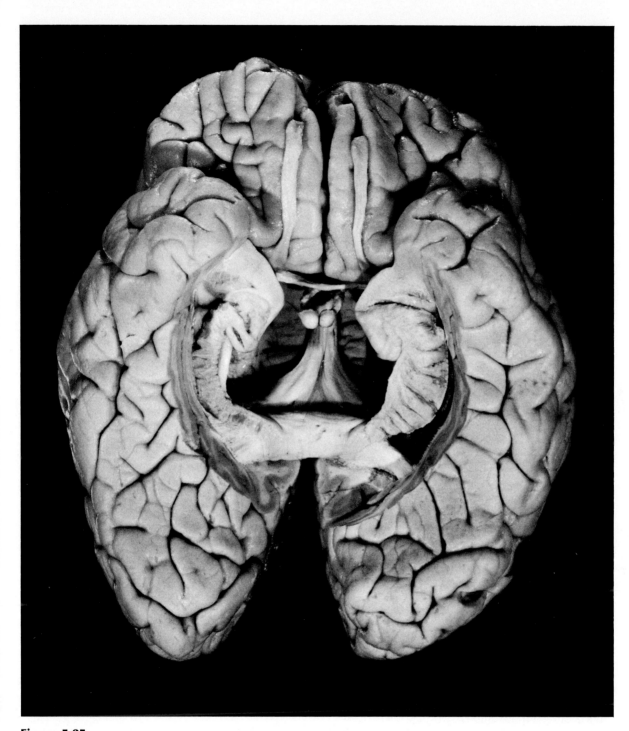

Figure 5-25.

5-26 Dentate gyri, amygdaloid bodies

A study of these structures has been made possible by removing the cerebellum, most of the brain stem, and the parahippocampal gyrus of each side, together with the subiculum (through which the hippocampus is continued into the cortex of the parahippocampal gyrus). At its anterior end, the dentate gyrus, named for the supposed resemblance of its notched medial margin to a row of teeth, turns abruptly in a backwards and medial direction to become the tail of the dentate gyrus. The fimbria of the hippocampus is a longitudinal band of white fibers which constitutes the efferent pathway from the hippocampus, including the dentate gyrus. Beneath the splenium of the corpus callosum, the dentate gyrus becomes flattened and smooth and continues on to the upper surface of the corpus callosum as the thin fasciolar gyrus. The latter is continuous with the indusium griseum, which covers the upper surface of the corpus callosum.

Lateral to the dentate gyrus, the temporal horn of the lateral ventricle has been opened to expose its choroid plexus, which is involved in the production of cerebrospinal fluid. The amygdaloid body is an ovoid gray nuclear mass, oriented transversely and with a slight posterior concavity. Lateral to the optic tract are the anterior (rostral) perforated substance, olfactory trigone, and olfactory striae. On the right side of the illustration the intermediate olfactory stria stands out clearly.

The midbrain has been transected at the level of the inferior (caudal) colliculi. The ventral aspect of the midbrain is nearer the front of the brain; the dorsal aspect of the midbrain is closer to the occipital lobes. Dorsomedial to the substantia nigra are the superior cerebellar peduncles and their decussation, and the medial longitudinal fasciculi lie dorsal to the previously mentioned decussation. The nuclei of the trochlear nerves are located ventral to the mesencephalic (cerebral) aqueduct. The root fibers arising from the trochlear nuclei form a decussation dorsal to the mesencephalic aqueduct, and they are the only cranial nerves that cross completely and that leave the dorsal aspect of the brain stem. Dorsolateral to the superior cerebellar peduncles are the somewhat dispersed fibers of the central tegmental tracts. The lateral portion of the tegmentum contains four lemnisci and has been referred to as the "sensory angle." Here the medial lemniscus is most ventral, the lateral lemniscus dorsal, and the intermediate area is occupied by the spinal and trigeminal lemnisci.

The pulvinar of the thalamus is seen dorsolateral to the midbrain, and the medial geniculate body can be recognized on its under surface. A short segment of the crus of the fornix is visible just medial to the pulvinar of the thalamus.

1. Olfactory bulb.
2. Orbital sulci and gyri.
3. Olfactory tract.
4. Straight gyrus.
5. Optic nerve.
6. Optic chiasma.
7. Olfactory trigone.
8. Medial olfactory gyrus with stria.

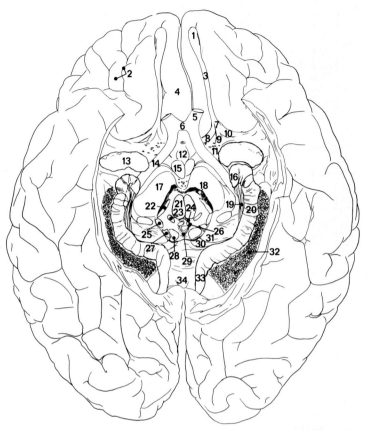

9. Intermediate olfactory stria.
10. Lateral olfactory gyrus with stria.
11. Anterior (rostral) perforated substance.
12. Tuber cinereum with infundibulum.
13. Amygdaloid nuclear complex.
14. Optic tract.
15. Mamillary body.
16. Tail of dentate gyrus.
17. Basis pedunculi.
18. Substantia nigra.
19. Fimbria of hippocampus.
20. Dentate gyrus.
21. Superior cerebellar peduncle.
22. Medial lemniscus.
23. Central tegmental tract.
24. Medial longitudinal fascicle.
25. Spinal and trigeminal lemnisci.
26. Trochlear nucleus.
27. Lateral lemniscus.
28. Nucleus of inferior (caudal) colliculus.
29. Decussation of trochlear nerves.
30. Crus of fornix.
31. Pulvinar of thalamus.
32. Choroid plexus in temporal horn of lateral ventricle.
33. Gyrus fasciolaris.
34. Splenium of corpus callosum.

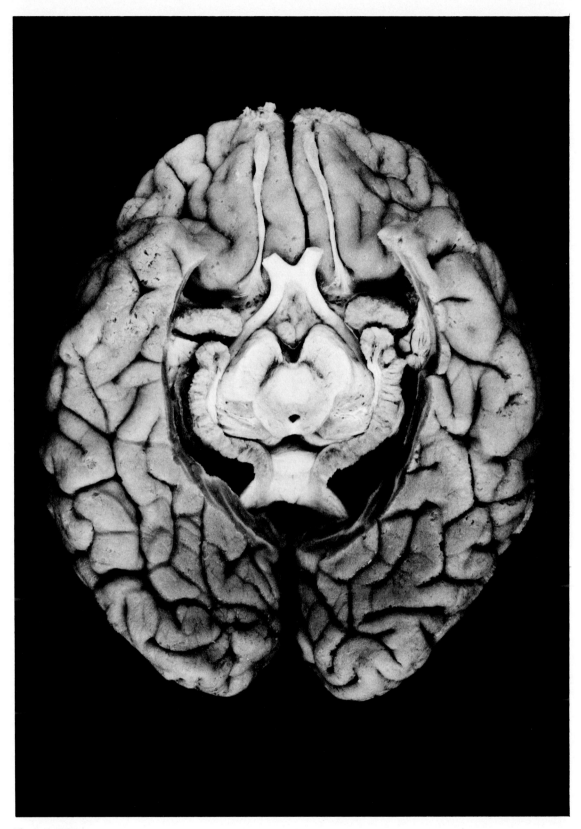

Figure 5-26.

The head of the caudate nucleus bulges into the frontal horn of the lateral ventricle, which is lined by ependyma. The groove between the caudate nucleus and the thalamus accommodates the thalamostriate vein and the stria terminalis. The septum pellucidum stretches across the interval between the genu of the corpus collosum and the columns of the fornix, separating the frontal horns of the two lateral ventricles. The thalamus has been cut at the level of its dorsal lateral nucleus. Although the lentiform nucleus is situated at a level lower than this section, narrow bands of gray matter that interconnect the caudate nucleus and the putamen are readily seen, separated by fascicles of the internal capsule. As can be seen in the left hemisphere, the choroid plexus protrudes into the central part of the lateral ventricle, and the route of entry of the plexus is via the choroid fissure, between the fornix and the lamina affixa. Traced backwards, the vascular tissue of the choroid plexus expands to form the choroid glomus. Here the temporal horn commences its downwards and lateral sweep around the posterior end of the thalamus.

In observing the white matter of the hemisphere, it is possible to follow the paths of various fiber systems because they are accompanied by numerous blood vessels. Close to the midline, note the divided anterior part of the corpus callosum with the fibers of the frontal forceps curving forwards from it, and, more posteriorly, the divided splenium of the corpus callosum with some fibers of the occipital forceps curving backwards from it.

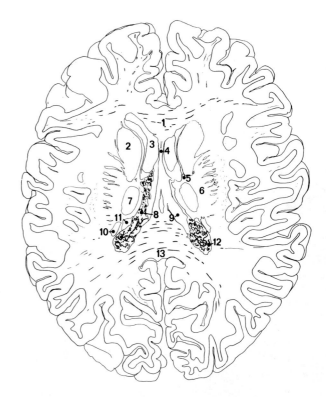

1. Genu of corpus callosum.
2. Head of caudate nucleus.
3. Frontal horn of lateral ventricle.
4. Septum pellicidum.
5. Thalamostriate vein.
6. Internal capsule.
7. Thalamus.
8. Choroid plexus of lateral ventricle.
9. Right crus of fornix.
10. Tail of caudate nucleus.
11. Stria terminalis.
12. Occipital horn of lateral ventricle.
13. Splenium of corpus callosum.

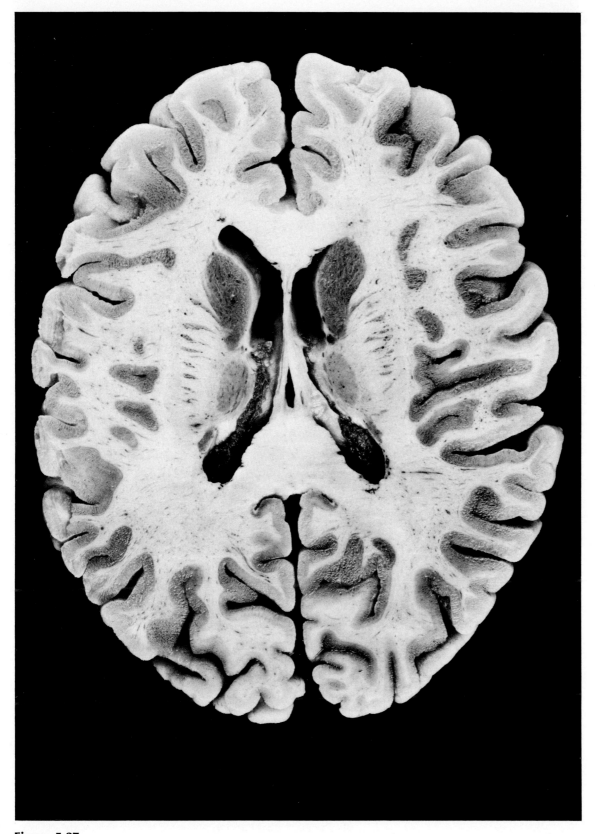

Figure 5-27.

This preparation permits recognition of the main nuclear masses of the thalamus. The internal medullary lamina is a well defined white band within the gray matter of the thalamus. This lamina is curved, with a pronounced medial concavity, and it separates the medial thalamic nuclei from the ventrolateral and posterior nuclei. Anteriorly it bifurcates to enclose the anterior nuclear group. Posteriorly it also bifurcates and surrounds another nuclear mass of the thalamus, the nucleus centromedianus. The ventrolateral thalamic nucleus is penetrated by numerous white fibers of the thalamic radiation. Its gray matter merges with that of the posterior nucleus, or pulvinar, which projects backwards.

Close to the midline, the habenular nucleus is connected anteriorly to the stria medullaris thalami. The putamen, a dark, ovoidal nuclear mass, is separated from the head of the caudate nucleus and the thalamus by the internal capsule. The retrolenticular part of the internal capsule, seen most clearly on the right side, is displaced laterally by the temporal horn of the lateral ventricle. Protruding into this horn of the lateral ventricle, through the choroid fissure, is the choroid plexus of the temporal horn, lying just lateral to the fimbria of the hippocampus. The configuration of white and gray matter of the dentate gyrus and hippocampus is distinctive.

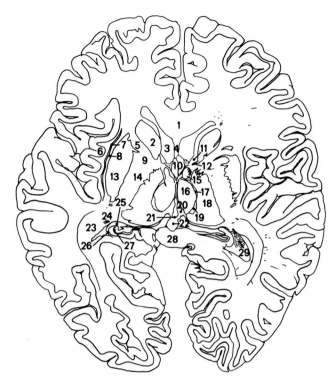

1. Genu of corpus callosum.
2. Head of caudate nucleus.
3. Frontal horn of lateral ventricle.
4. Septum pellucidum.
5. Anterior limb of internal capsule.
6. Cortex of insula.
7. Claustrum.
8. External capsule.
9. Genu of internal capsule.
10. Columns of fornix.
11. Stria terminalis.
12. Thalamostriate vein.
13. Putamen.
14. Posterior limb of internal capsule.
15. Anterior thalamic nuclear group.
16. Medial thalamic nucleus.
17. Internal medullary lamina of thalamus.
18. Lateral thalamic nuclear group.
19. Centromedian thalamic nucleus.
20. Habenular nucleus.
21. Habenular commissure.
22. Pineal body.
23. Retrolenticular part of internal capsule.
24. Tail of caudate nucleus.
25. Fimbria of hippocampus.
26. Alveus of hippocampus.
27. Hippocampus.
28. Splenium of corpus callosum.
29. Choroid plexus in temporal horn of lateral ventricle.

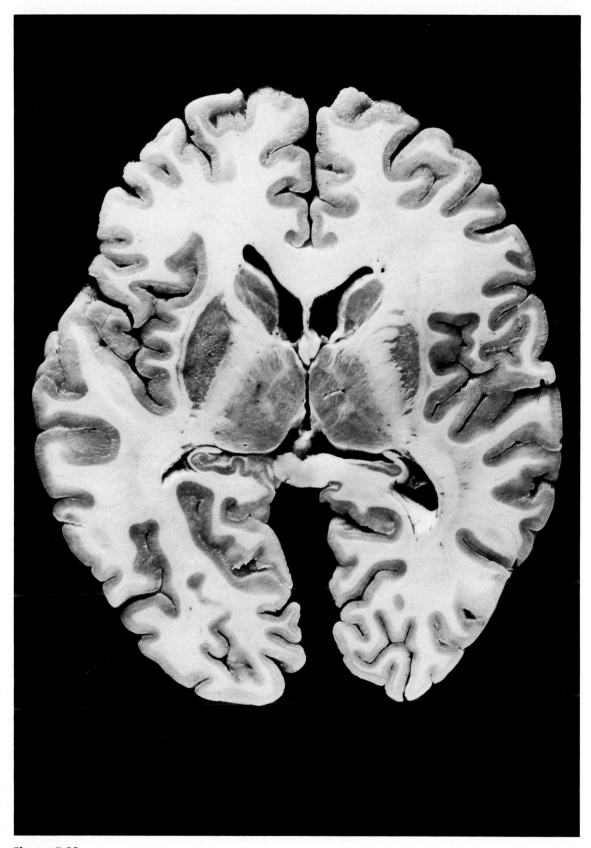

Figure 5-28.

The oval, dark gray head of the caudate nucleus bulges into the frontal horn of the lateral ventricle and is separated from the putamen by the internal capsule (anterior limb). The elongated putamen is equally dark, whereas the globus pallidus appears as a smaller, wedge-shaped, pale mass, contiguous with the genu of the internal capsule. The dark appearance of the caudate nucleus and putamen is attributable to their content of blood vessels and neuronal cell bodies. Numerous myelinated fibers traversing the globus pallidus make the latter much paler.

This section passes through the inferior part of the thalamus and only a small part of the medial nucleus is visible, together with the ventrolateral thalamic nuclear group. Note the very long retrolenticular portion of the internal capsule containing fibers of the optic radiation: on their way to be distributed to occipital lobe cortex, these fibers curve around the lateral wall of the temporal horn of the lateral ventricle.

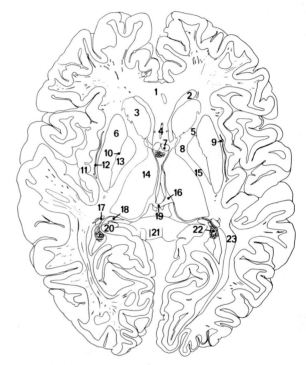

1. Genu of corpus callosum.
2. Frontal horn of lateral ventricle.
3. Head of caudate nucleus.
4. Septum pellucidum.
5. Anterior limb of internal capsule.
6. Putamen.
7. Column of fornix.
8. Genu of internal capsule.
9. External capsule.
10. Lateral medullary lamina.
11. Cortex of insula.
12. Claustrum.
13. Globus pallidus.
14. Thalamus.
15. Posterior limb of internal capsule.
16. Habenular nucleus.
17. Tail of caudate nucleus.
18. Fimbria of hippocampus.
19. Habenular commissure.
20. Hippocampus.
21. Splenium of corpus callosum.
22. Choroid plexus in temporal horn of lateral ventricle.
23. Retrolenticular part of internal capsule.

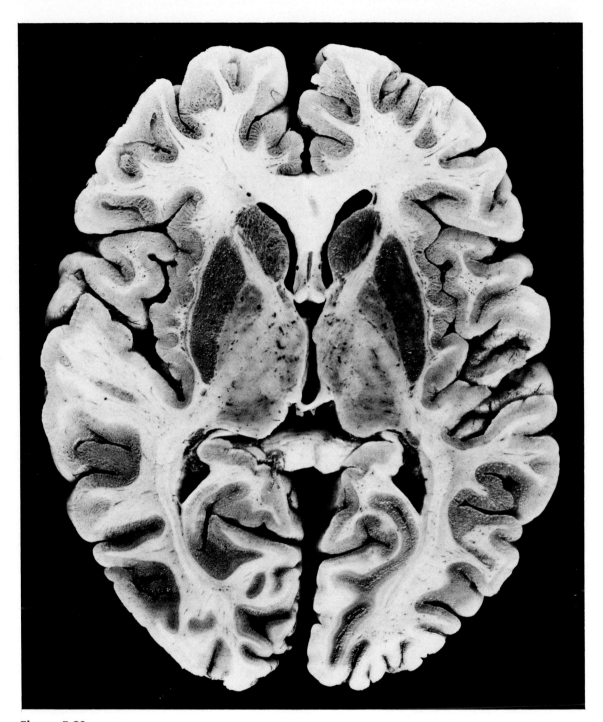

Figure 5-29.

The septum pellucidum is the middlemost structure, and separates the two frontal horns of the lateral ventricles. The septum is attached superiorly to the **genu** and inferiorly to the **rostrum** of the corpus callosum. Note that the gray matter of the caudate nucleus continues uninterrupted into the putamen, through a prolongation just inferior to the internal capsule (anterior limb). Also note the gray connections between the caudate nucleus and the putamen, which interrupt the fascicles of the anterior limb of the internal capsule. Putamen and caudate are one mass of gray matter, partially separated by these internal capsule fibers.

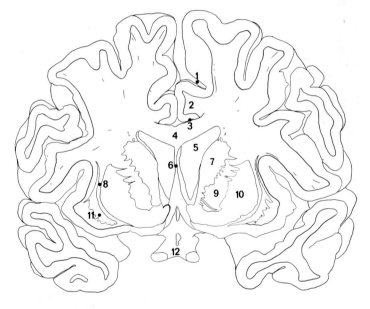

1. Cingulate sulcus.
2. Cingulate gyrus.
3. Callosal sulcus.
4. Body of corpus callosum.
5. Frontal horn of lateral ventricle.
6. Septum pellucidum.
7. Head of caudate nucleus.
8. External capsule.
9. Anterior limb of internal capsule.
10. Putamen.
11. Claustrum.
12. Optic chiasma.

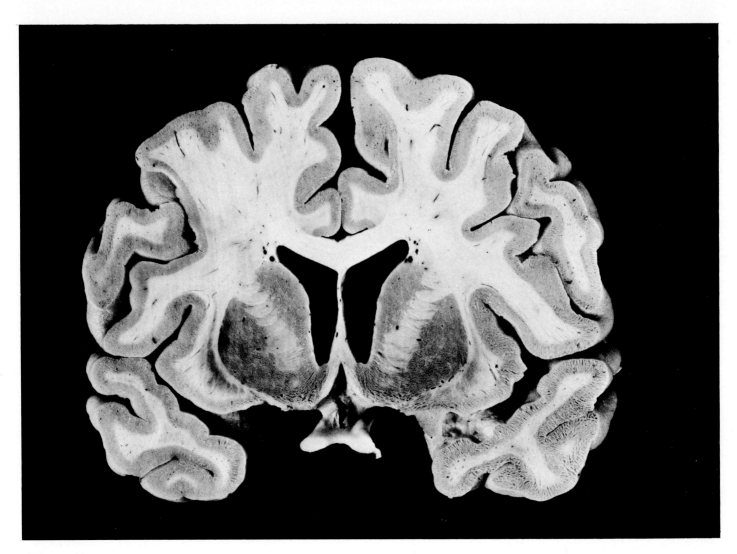

Figure 5-30.

The solid, **median** part of the anterior commissure is most clearly visible below the columns of the fornix. Both columns of the fornix are found, together with the median part of the anterior commissure, in the anterior wall of the 3rd ventricle with a small triangular recess between them. The lower margin of the septum pellucidum is attached to the columns of the fornix. The lateral part of the anterior commissure traverses the inferior part of the corpus striatum. On both sides note the vascular channels that pass from the anterior (rostral) perforated substance into the gray substance of the corpus striatum. These are important striate branches of the middle cerebral artery, destined for the corpus striatum, internal capsule and associated structures.

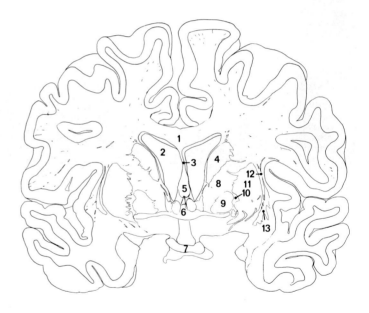

1. Body of corpus callosum.
2. Frontal horn of lateral ventricle.
3. Septum pellucidum.
4. Body of caudate nucleus.
5. Columns of fornix.
6. Anterior (rostral) commissure.
7. Optic chiasma.
8. Anterior limb of internal capsule.
9. Globus pallidus.
10. Lateral medullary lamina.
11. Putamen.
12. External capsule.
13. Claustrum.

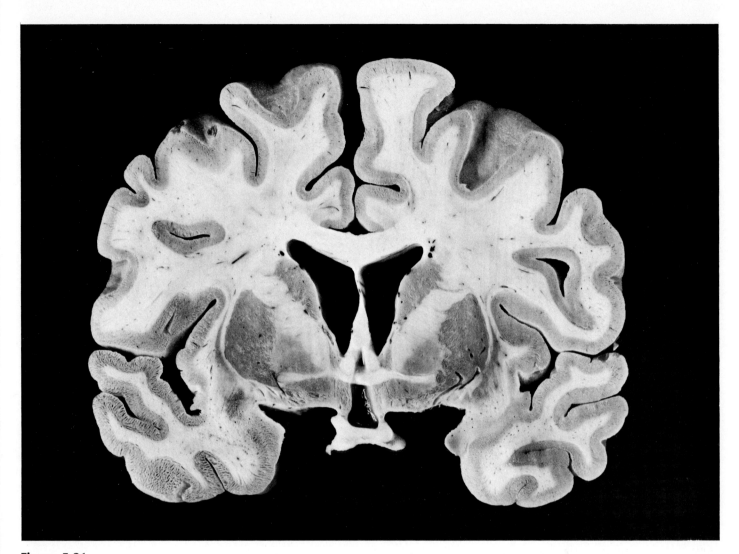

Figure 5-31.

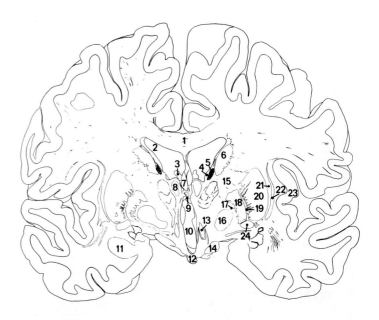

This section passes through the central part of the lateral ventricle, close to its prolongation forwards as the frontal horn. In the floor of the lateral ventricle, close to the midline, is the anterior thalamic nuclear group, bounded on both sides by the internal medullary lamina of the thalamus. Just medial to the body of the caudate nucleus is the conspicuous thalamostriate vein, its medial edge overlapped by the stria terminalis. There is continuity between the choroid plexuses of the 3rd and the lateral ventricles. The 3rd ventricle is a vertically oriented slit which has a small ventral extension (the infundibular recess). Lateral to the massive anterior limb of the internal capsule are the three parts of the lentiform nucleus, namely the internal and external parts of the globus pallidus and the putamen. These three are separated from each other by the medial and lateral medullary laminae of the globus pallidus. The dark putamen contrasts sharply with the globus pallidus.

1. Body of corpus callosum.
2. Central part of lateral ventricle.
3. Choroid plexus of lateral ventricle.
4. Stria terminalis.
5. Thalamostriate vein.
6. Body of caudate nucleus.
7. Column of fornix.
8. Anterior thalamic nuclear group.
9. Tela choroidea and choroid plexus of 3rd ventricle.
10. 3rd ventricle.
11. Amygdaloid nuclear complex.
12. Tuber cinereum.
13. Column of fornix.
14. Optic tract.
15. Genu of internal capsule.
16. Medial part of globus pallidus.
17. Medial medullary lamina.
18. Lateral part of globus pallidus.
19. Lateral medullary lamina.
20. Putamen.
21. External capsule.
22. Claustrum.
23. Cortex of insula.
24. Anterior (rostral) commissure.

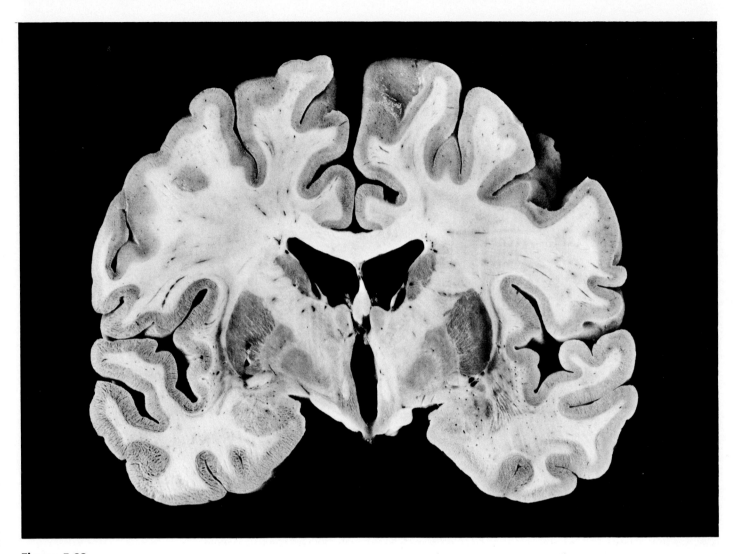

Figure 5-32.

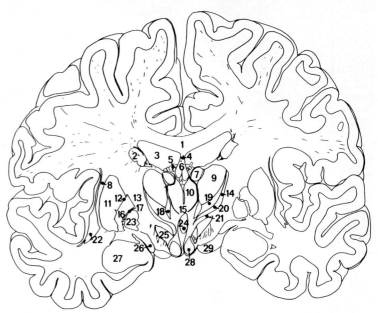

The hypothalamus can be divided into an anterior (supra-optic) zone, an intermediate (infundibulotuberal) zone and a posterior (mamillary) zone (through which this section passes). A number of thalamic nuclei can be recognized in this section, separated from each other by the internal medullary lamina, which accommodates the mamillothalamic fasciculus as the latter passes from the prominent medial nucleus of the mamillary body to the anterior thalamic nuclear group. The latter nuclear group is lodged within the cranial bifurcation of the internal medullary lamina. The medial thalamic nuclei are small, circumscribed gray masses situated adjacent to the lateral wall of the 3rd ventricle. The lateral thalamic nuclear group is much larger. Immediately lateral to this nuclear group is a relatively indistinct layer of intermingled gray and white matter. This layer is termed the reticular nucleus of the thalamus, and it merges ventromedially with a small collection of gray matter called the zona incerta. Note the white areas above and below the zona incerta, sometimes referred to as the H_1, H_2, and H_3 fields (or areas) of Forel respectively. Forel's fields contain—though not exclusively—discharge pathways from the globus pallidus to the thalamus. Immediately below the H_2 field of Forel is the subthalamic nucleus, which is prominent only in primates including man. A lesion of one subthalamic nucleus may result in hemiballismus, which is characterized by sudden, violent movements of one or both limbs on the side opposite the lesion. Components of the lentiform nucleus (internal and external parts of the globus pallidus, and the putamen) are seen lateral to the posterior limb of the internal capsule.

In the temporal lobe the large, oval gray mass, the amygdaloid body, receives its name from its supposed resemblance to an almond. Its ventral and lateral aspects are well demarcated by white matter. More dorsally there is incomplete separation of the amygdaloid body from the putamen and globus pallidus and it is applied closely to the optic tract. The

1. Body of corpus callosum.
2. Body of caudate nucleus.
3. Central part of lateral ventricle.
4. Septum pellucidum.
5. Choroid plexus of lateral ventricle.
6. Columns of fornix.
7. Anterior thalamic nuclear group.
8. External capsule.
9. Lateral thalamic nuclear group.
10. Medial thalamic nucleus.
11. Putamen.
12. Lateral medullary lamina.
13. Internal capsule.
14. Reticular thalamic nuclei.
15. Interthalamic adhesion.
16. Lateral part of globus pallidus.
17. Medial medullary lamina.
18. Mamillothalamic fascicle.
19. H_1 field of Forel.
20. Zona incerta.
21. H_2 field of Forel.
22. Claustrum.
23. Medial part of globus pallidus.
24. 3rd ventricle.
25. Hypothalamic nucleus.
26. Optic tract.
27. Amygdaloid nuclear complex.
28. Mamillary body.
29. Basis pedunculi.

best known outflow tract of the amygdaloid nuclear complex, the stria terminalis, emerges from the caudal end of the amygdala and follows the medial side of the tail of the caudate nucleus backwards, upwards and then forwards. In this section it occupies the shallow groove that separates the body of the caudate nucleus from the thalamus.

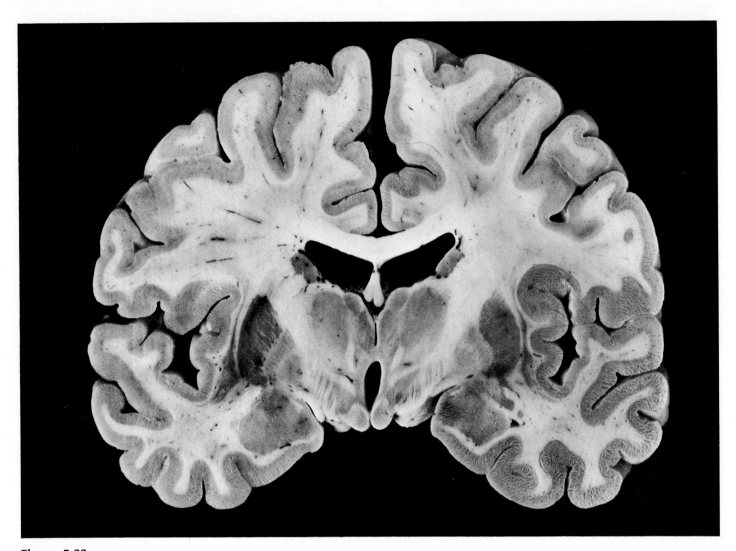

Figure 5-33.

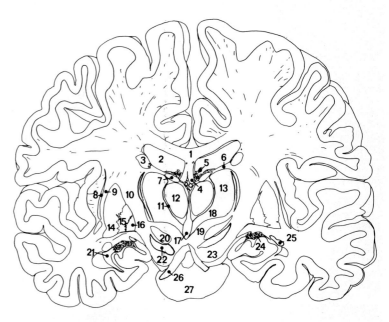

Certain thalamic nuclei can be distinguished in this section, separated from each other by the highly curved internal medullary lamina. The medial nucleus is dark and circumscribed, whereas the lateral nuclear group is much paler. The anterior nuclear group is small and flattened, and is situated more laterally on the dorsal surface of the thalamus. The reticular nuclei of the thalamus can be identified, but the zona incerta is difficult to see on this section. The H₁ field (or area) of Forel, containing the ansa lenticularis, is a rather large zone of white matter. The ansa lenticularis contains a multitude of axons which stream out and end in the ventral anterolateral thalamic nucleus (which can also be seen in this section). The subthalamic nucleus is an identifiable nodule of gray matter that lies above and medial to the substantia nigra.

Corticofugal fibers at the base of the corona radiata pass directly into the basis pedunculi via the posterior limb of the internal capsule. Fibers of the optic and auditory radiations are interposed between the lentiform nucleus above and the temporal horn of the lateral ventricle below. Other structures seen in the roof of the temporal horn of the lateral ventricle are the tail of the caudate nucleus and the stria terminalis.

1. Body of corpus callosum.
2. Central part of lateral ventricle.
3. Tail of caudate nucleus.
4. Body of fornix.
5. Choroid plexus of lateral ventricle.
6. Stria terminalis.
7. Anterior thalamic nuclear group.
8. Claustrum.
9. External capsule.
10. Internal capsule.
11. Internal medullary lamina of thalamus.
12. Medial thalamic nucleus.
13. Dorsal lateral thalamic nucleus.
14. Putamen.
15. Lateral part of globus pallidus.
16. Medial part of globus pallidus.
17. 3rd ventricle.
18. Ventral anterolateral thalamic nucleus.
19. H₁ field of Forel.
20. Subthalamic nucleus.
21. Alveus of hippocampus.
22. Substantia nigra.
23. Basis pedunculi.
24. Choroid plexus of temporal horn of lateral ventricle.
25. Tail of caudate nucleus.
26. Oculomotor nerve.
27. Pons.

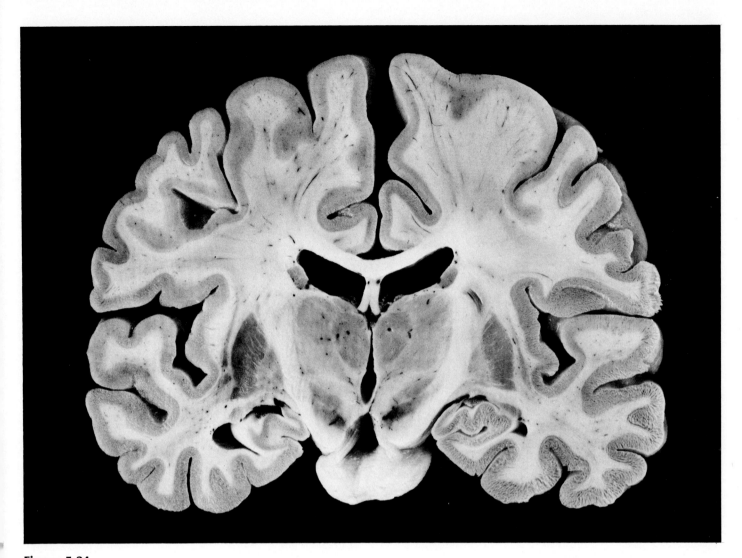

Figure 5-34.

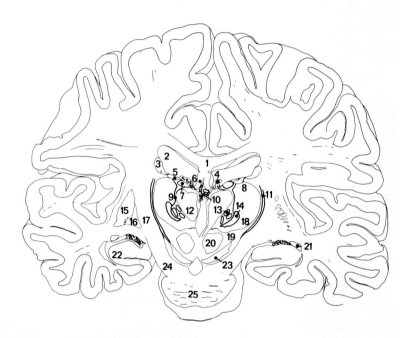

The fornix is seen touching the corpus callosum. The lentiform nucleus is present only on the left side of the illustration. The anterior nuclear group of the thalamus is here located more laterally than in a more anterior slice (Fig. 5-34). The anterior nuclear group of the thalamus can be distinguished by its location within a dorsal bifurcation of the internal medullary lamina. The ventral bifurcation of the internal medullary lamina envelops the nucleus centromedianus of the thalamus. The choroid plexus of the 3rd ventricle is united with the choroid plexus of the lateral ventricle via the choroid fissure between thalamus and fornix. Note the two large internal cerebral veins in the tela choroidea of the 3rd ventricle.

The red nuclei appear as large, spherical portions of gray matter, related to the concavity of the substantia nigra. Lateral to the red nucleus, the trigeminal, the spinal, and medial lemnisci show as a white area. These lemnisci terminate in the ventral posteromedial and posterolateral thalamic nuclei respectively, and these are clearly visible in this preparation. On each side the basis pedunculi, containing corticospinal and corticopontine projection fibers, can be identified.

1. Body of corpus callosum.
2. Central part of lateral ventricle.
3. Tail of caudate nucleus.
4. Choroid plexus of lateral ventricle.
5. Stria terminalis.
6. Crus of fornix.
7. Anterior thalamic nuclear group.
8. Dorsal lateral thalamic nucleus.
9. Internal medullary lamina of thalamus.
10. Choroid plexus of 3rd ventricle.
11. Reticular thalamic nuclei.
12. Medial thalamic nucleus.
13. Centromedian thalamic nucleus.
14. Ventral posteromedial (arcuate) thalamic nucleus.
15. Putamen.
16. Globus pallidus.
17. Internal capsule.
18. Ventral posterolateral thalamic nucleus.
19. Medial, spinal, and trigeminal lemnisci.
20. Red nucleus.
21. Tail of caudate nucleus.
22. Hippocampus.
23. Substantia nigra.
24. Basis pedunculi.
25. Pons.

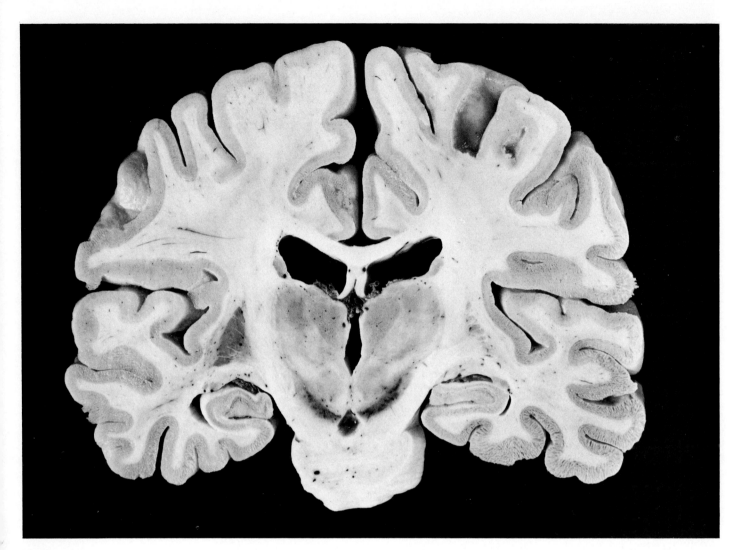

Figure 5-35.

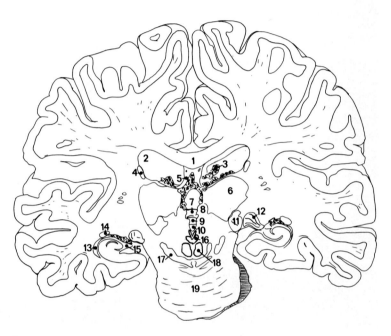

The section is slightly oblique and shows the disposition of many important structures. 1) In the midline, below the crura of the fornix, is the small posterior part of the 3rd ventricle together with its tela choroidea and its vascular fringed choroid plexus, which projects downwards as an invagination of the roof of the 3rd ventricle, on each side of the midline. 2) The thalami are sectioned at the level of the posterior (epithalamic) nucleus (pulvinar). 3) The preparation shows both habenular and posterior commissures, with the pineal recess between them. On the right side of the illustration, medial and lateral geniculate bodies—which together constitute the metathalamus—can be recognized. It may be observed that the lateral geniculate nucleus is organized in alternating gray and white laminae. 4) The oculomotor nuclei, together with their parasympathetic accessory nuclei (of Edinger-Westphal), are located ventral to the mesencephalic (cerebral) aqueduct and dorsal to the superior cerebellar peduncles. 5) The surfaces of the cerebral hemispheres show complex cerebral convolutions of the parietal and temporal lobes. Insular cortex is visible also, particularly on the left side of the illustration. The hippocampus and associated structures abut the medial and inferior surface of the temporal horn of the lateral ventricle.

1. Body of corpus callosum.
2. Central part of lateral ventricle.
3. Choroid plexus of lateral ventricle.
4. Tail of caudate nucleus.
5. Crus of fornix.
6. Posterior thalamic nucleus (pulvinar).
7. Habenular commissure.
8. Habenular nucleus.
9. Posterior (epithalamic) commissure.
10. Cerebral aqueduct.
11. Medial geniculate nucleus.
12. Lateral geniculate nucleus.
13. Temporal horn of lateral ventricle.
14. Tail of caudate nucleus.
15. Fimbria of hippocampus.
16. Oculomotor nucleus.
17. Substantia nigra.
18. Superior cerebellar peduncle above decussation.
19. Pons.

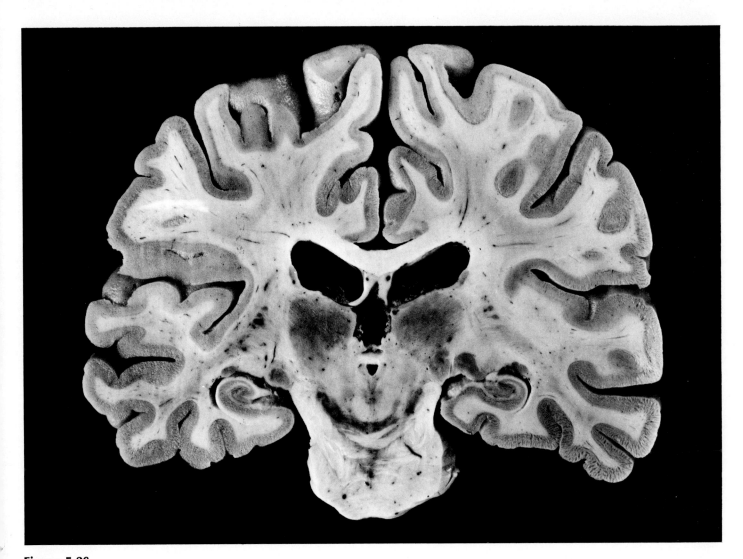

Figure 5-36.

BIBLIOGRAPHY

Barr ML: The Human Nervous System, An Anatomic Viewpoint. Hagerstown, Harper & Row, 1979

Carpenter MB: Core Text of Neuroanatomy, 2nd ed. Baltimore, Williams & Wilkins, 1978

DeArmond SJ, Fusco MM, Dewey MM: Structure of the Human Brain; a Photographic Atlas. New York, Oxford University Press, 1976

Dunkerley GB: A Basic Atlas of the Human Nervous System. Philadelphia, F.A. Davis, 1975

Everett NB: Functional Neuroanatomy, 6th ed. Philadelphia, Lea & Febiger, 1971

Feneis H: Anatomische Bildnomenklatur. Stuttgart, Georg Thieme Verlag, 1967

Ford DH, Schadè JP: Atlas of the Human Brain. 2nd Rev. ed. New York, Elsevier Publishing Company, 1971

Ingram RW: A Review of Anatomical Neurology. Baltimore, University Park Press, 1976

Ludwig E, Klinger J: Atlas Cerebri Humani. Boston, Little, Brown & Company, 1956

Matzke, HA, Foltz FM: Synopsis of Neuroanatomy. New York, Oxford University Press, 1967

Noback CR, Demarest RJ: The Nervous System, Introduction and Review. New York, McGraw-Hill, 1977

Roberts MJ, Hanaway J: Atlas of the Human Brain in Section. Philadelphia, Lea & Febiger, 1970

Rohen YW: Funktionelle Anatomie des Nervensystems. Stuttgart, F. K. Schattauerverlag, 1975

Sinelnikow RD: Atlas of the Human Anatomy, Vol III, Nervous System, Organs of Special Senses and Endocrynology. Moskva, Gosudarstvenoe Izdatelstvo Medicinskoy Literaturi, 1963

Talmage L: The Neuroanatomic Basis for Clinical Neurology. New York, McGraw-Hill, 1977

Truex RC, Carpenter MB: Human Neuroanatomy, 7th ed. Baltimore, Williams & Wilkins, 1976

Watson C: Basic Human Neuroanatomy, An Introductory Atlas. Boston, Little, Brown & Company, 1977

Warwick R, Williams PL: Gray's Anatomy. Philadelphia, Lea & Febiger, 1973

Williams PL, Warwick R: Functional Neuroanatomy of Man. Philadelphia, W.B. Saunders, 1975

Wolf–Heidegger G: Atlas of Systematic Human Anatomy, Systema Nervosum-Systema Vasorum. New York, S. Karger, 1972

Wright MK: Fibre Systems of the Brain and Spinal Cord. Johannesburg, Witwatersrand University Press, 1959

Zuleger S, Staubesand Y: Atlas of the Central Nervous System in Sectional Planes. Baltimore, Urban and Schwarzenberg, 1977

INDEX